26332

Daumier

Don Quixote and Sancho Panza (97), *Courtauld Institute of Art*

Daumier

PAINTINGS AND DRAWINGS

An exhibition organized by

the Arts Council of Great Britain

at the Tate Gallery

The Arts Council of Great Britain 1961

The exhibition will be open from June 14th to July 30th, 1961

Mondays, Wednesdays, Fridays and Saturdays, 10 to 6,

Tuesdays and Thursdays, 10 to 8, Sundays 2 to 6

Designed and printed in England at The Curwen Press, Plaistow, E.13

Foreword

For a number of years the Arts Council has considered arranging a small exhibition of Daumier's work, including sculpture and lithographs, at its own gallery in St James's Square. The initial suggestion was made in 1958 by Mr Alan Bowness, who was to have organized the exhibition on the Council's behalf. After consultation with Mr K. E. Maison however, who is at present engaged on a catalogue raisonné of the artist's work, he expressed the opinion that it would be preferable to embark instead on a major representative exhibition of the paintings and drawings only. This would naturally take considerably more time to assemble and we therefore invited Mr Maison (who had long wished to produce such an exhibition) to undertake the charge. The Council was fortunate in securing so unrivalled an authority for the purpose and we are deeply grateful to him for the untiring energy he has devoted to the exhibition. Mr Maison has not only selected and catalogued the exhibits, but he has been personally responsible for securing almost all the loans, a task that entailed lengthy correspondence and visits to several countries. Many of the works shown here, and particularly those from private collections in France and the United States, are virtually unknown in this country and some of them have not been exhibited before. The exhibition contains the largest assembly of Daumier's paintings ever to be seen under one roof since the 1901 exhibition at the Ecole des Beaux-Arts in Paris; Mr Maison, moreover, throws a new light in this catalogue on the difficult problems of dating and authenticity.

That it has been possible to present so comprehensive a survey of Daumier's *œuvre* as a painter and draughtsman is due to the splendid response from lenders. They are too numerous to mention individually, but their names will be found at the end of this catalogue. Their generosity, which in many cases has entailed a considerable sacrifice, is warmly appreciated and we are especially grateful to such institutions as the Museum Boymans-van Beuningen, Rotterdam, the Corporation of Glasgow and the National Museum of Wales which have entrusted us with a large number of works and also to others, such as the Museum Folkwang, Essen, which have parted with particularly rare examples.

The exhibition has been organized under the sponsorship of the Association Française d'Action Artistique, and we wish to express our gratitude to His Excellency Monsieur Jean Chauvel, the French Ambassador in London, Monsieur Philippe Erlanger and Monsieur F. Gobin, of the Association, and Monsieur Cyrille Arnavon and Miss Renée Cameron, of the French Embassy, for their assistance. We are also grateful to the Directors of museums and galleries who have put Mr Maison in touch with owners; to Madame Jacqueline Marette, of the International Council of Museums, Paris, and Mr N. M. Hallett, First Secretary and Consul at the British Embassy, Buenos Aires, for assistance in the transport arrangements. Lastly, we wish to record our thanks to Mr Alan Bowness who has written the interesting introduction to this catalogue, and to the Director and Trustees of the Tate Gallery who have made available not only the usual exhibition galleries but also the additional space we required.

GABRIEL WHITE

Daumier the Painter

by Alan Bowness

Shortly after Honoré Daumier's death on 11 February 1879, one of his obituarists wrote that 'as a painter he was esteemed more by artists of the first rank than by the public. His bold and powerful pictures have obtained much less success than their merit deserves although they were admired as masterpieces by Delacroix, Daubigny, Dupré.' Today there would be no difficulty in continuing this list. From Delacroix on to Cézanne and to Picasso, artists have always been ready to recognize Daumier as one of the greatest of nineteenth-century painters and perhaps the outstanding draughtsman of the period. And yet what the obituarist said remains true: Daumier has never won commensurate public admiration.

There are obvious explanations for this. His life was comparatively uneventful and offers no opportunity for the Romantic myth-making that has resulted in Van Gogh and Lautrec becoming popular culture heroes. But more important and more serious, Daumier's work as a painter has always been overshadowed by his reputation as a caricaturist or, as we should say today, a cartoonist. As we shall see, this told against him in several different ways. The paintings were much in advance of their time and, as Daumier was incapable of giving them the kind of finish his contemporaries expected, were often dismissed as being unfinished or merely sketches. This originality as an artist and the early popularity he won for his newspaper work combined to prevent people taking his paintings seriously. Daumier was caught in a vicious circle; to earn a livelihood he had to continue producing cartoons when he would have much preferred to use the time for painting. The very success he won as a young man for his cartoons worked to his disfavour. By 1835 at the age of 27 he found himself imprisoned by the demands of weekly journalism, expected to produce two or three cartoons every week. Once or twice he tried to break away from this drudgery and establish himself as a painter, but without success. When, around 1856, he was introduced to a young aspirant, Daumier asked him why he wished to be a cartoonist and said, 'for thirty years I've always been hoping that I've done the last one'. It is sad to record that in 1872 he was still turning out lithographs—there are 4,000 in Delteil's great catalogue—when encroaching blindness forced him to stop work.

By comparison his painted *œuvre* is small: his first biographer Arsène Alexandre described it as 'a hundred pictures and as many studies'. It will be easily appreciated, therefore, that in this exhibition Mr Maison has succeeded in gathering together an altogether remarkable proportion of Daumier's surviving paintings and drawings—very much larger than at any other Daumier exhibition held since his death, except that at Paris in 1901, when 112 oils and 354 other items, mostly drawings, were shown. In size and proportion the Arts Council's exhibition follows very closely that arranged by Daumier's friends at the Durand-Ruel galleries in Paris in the last year of his life: on that occasion 94 oils and 147 drawings and water-colours were exhibited.

In 1878, unlike almost all later Daumier exhibitions, only a handful of lithographs and sculptures were shown alongside the pictures. Daumier's friends wanted to show the general public what he had achieved as a painter: they wanted his great (and entirely justified) reputation as a cartoonist to be forgotten for a moment in order that his full stature as an artist could be revealed. This practice has been followed here in 1961, and perhaps at last the public will follow the artists, and give these bold and powerful pictures the popular approbation they richly deserve.

Honoré Daumier was born in Marseilles on 26 February 1808. His father was by trade a glazier and frame-maker who sometimes restored pictures; but he also wrote verse plays on historical themes, and his ambition was to be recognized as a poet. To further his literary career Jean-Baptiste Daumier took his family to Paris in 1816, and here his son grew up and spent the greater part of his life. From the age of twelve Daumier had to earn a living, and he seems to have worked as an office boy for a bailiff and as a book-shop assistant for a short while before he was allowed to study art. He learnt the rudiments of drawing from Alexandre Lenoir, and then worked in the Académie Suisse for a time, no doubt acquiring that mastery of the figure which is apparent in his earliest works.

From 1817 the new technique of lithography had attracted many of the younger artists, including Delacroix and Géricault and Charlet, whose prints did much to keep Napoleon's fame alive. It was perhaps natural that a young man with Daumier's gifts and no financial means

6

should be drawn to lithography, and from 1825 to 1830 he worked as a studio assistant in the workshop of the printer Belliard, learning how to prepare the stones for the lithographic portraits that Belliard published.

He had complete technical control of his medium by June 1830 when revolution broke out and the reactionary king, Charles X, was driven off the throne, and replaced by the 'bourgeois' monarch, Louis-Philippe. As the new regime grew rapidly more and more reactionary, Daumier's reformist sympathies were outraged, and he readily put his art at the service of the young liberals who were opposed to the government and the king. In a series of brilliant and hard-hitting caricatures and cartoons that appeared in the left-wing press in 1830 and 1831 Daumier established a reputation as the outstanding political cartoonist of the day. His career was briefly interrupted when he was charged with sedition and sentenced to six months in the Ste Pélagie prison, but on his release in February 1833, Daumier, undeterred, continued much as before. In August 1835 the government took action, and instituted a strict Press censorship which effectively suppressed *La Caricature*, one of the weekly papers for which Daumier worked. Another, *Le Charivari*, turned from political satire to criticism of bourgeois society, and this was the direction in which Daumier's art moved. In 1836 the first *Robert Macaire* cartoon appeared, and in a long series of plates Daumier lampooned the characteristic figures of the newly emergent and rapidly developing capitalist society of which he deeply disapproved.

The *Robert Macaire* cartoons were very successful: Daumier himself later disliked them, probably because they had won such great popular favour. For this, added to the fame of the political cartoons, stamped Daumier indelibly in the public mind as a cartoonist and made it ever more difficult for him to earn a reputation as a more serious artist.

That this was his ambition is, I think, beyond question. There is some evidence however for believing that Daumier thought more about sculpture than painting in the early part of his career. When he came out of prison in 1833 he went to live in an artists' phalanstery established by a number of his friends, among them the painters Diaz and Jeanron and the sculptor Auguste Préault. Préault, who was two years younger than Daumier, produced some extraordinary works in the early 1830s, among them the *Tuerie* relief now in the Louvre. Given more favourable circumstances he might have developed into the great sculptor of Romanticism, but his work was systematically refused by the Salon juries and his talent stultified through lack of opportunity.

Préault certainly aroused Daumier's interest in sculpture, but the cartoonist could see that his friend's position was no happier than his own. The possibility of any original achievement in sculpture was very slight in an art world dominated by reactionaries with every commission and every exhibition under their control. Daumier himself made a few remarkable pieces of sculpture, notably the *Emigrants* relief (see No. 106) and the figure of Ratapoil, and, what is more important, he brought a sculptor's feeling for form to his painting.

The artistic establishment's suppression of Préault's work was matched by their treatment of Théodore Rousseau, whose landscapes were year after year refused by the Salon juries. Daumier must have realized from this that he would find it very difficult ever to succeed as a painter as long as he remained a notorious member of the political and artistic opposition. He probably painted very little before 1848: his annual production of lithographs at this period was high, and he could not have had much time for painting. Some of the works ascribed to the early part of Daumier's career are of doubtful authenticity, others are of little artistic consequence, and none are shown in the exhibition. Among the earliest pictures *The Moonlight Walk* (No. 78) is perhaps the most characteristic and best known, and this, by comparison with the later work, is still only halfway towards painting.

The revolution of February 1848 brought Daumier his opportunity to change careers. Under the Second Republic the artistic life of France was for a short time run by Daumier's friends, whose years of opposition were thus rewarded. When the 1848 Salon opened, everything submitted was hung: Courbet showed ten paintings and suddenly found himself famous, Millet showed *The Winnower*, which was at once purchased by the Minister of Fine Arts and set the pattern for the official art of the new Republic. Daumier did not exhibit, which makes one suspect that he had not yet begun to paint seriously.

On 18 March 1848 the Ministry of Fine Arts announced a public competition for a figure symbolic of the new republic. Daumier's friends seem to have decided that this was his great chance. Courbet, more than ten years Daumier's junior, went with the painter Bonvin to see Daumier and persuade him to take part. Daumier made a sketch on

Honoré Daumier, from a photograph by Nadar, *c.* 1865

canvas (now in the Louvre) which was placed eleventh out of the twenty works short-listed at the preliminary judging on 12 June, and he was asked to paint a picture for the final competition. His friends— not only the painters, but critics like Champfleury and Gautier—were determined that he should win. In his review of the exhibition of the short-listed designs, Champfleury speaks of 'one simple and serious canvas in a ridiculous competition'.

Daumier however could not produce a finished picture, and this inability to take his work beyond the stage of a sketch helps to account for his failure to establish himself as a painter. The question of finish was obviously a problem that worried him: it is significant that one of the two entries relating to Daumier in Delacroix's *Journal* reads: 'M. Baudelaire came in . . . He told me of the difficulties that Daumier experiences in finishing' (5 February 1849). This particular difficulty represents an important moment of crisis in the whole history of nineteenth-century painting, and what was Daumier's undoing in his own time is today seen as part of his greatness.

Despite his difficulties over the *Republic* picture, Daumier began work in 1848 on a painting celebrating the February Revolution, or perhaps the Four June Days when the insurrection of the unemployed demanding the right to work was put down with brutal ruthlessness by General Cavaignac—a significant step towards the recantation of the principles of the February Revolution. Three large oil sketches of *The Riot*, or *The Family on the Barricade* are known, together with some studies for individual figures, such as No. 39 in this exhibition. It seems reasonably certain that Daumier was hoping for an official commission to treat the subject on a more ambitious scale.

The question of art patronage by the short-lived second Republic is an obscure one which needs to be studied in detail, as it resulted in the creation (or crystallization) of a new style, Realism, which was the death-blow to Romanticism. It is certainly a lesson about the importance such a political change can have on art: there is no doubt that the careers of Courbet, Millet and Daumier were completely transformed. State patronage was not something new, but not since the days of David had the progressive artist so much to expect from the agents of the government. The artist was to be given the opportunity of working for society at large, not for individual patrons; his pictures were to be purchased or even commissioned by the State, shown at exhibitions, and then placed in some permanent public collection. It is quite clear from Courbet's behaviour, for example, that he expected a startling development in facilities for exhibition, especially of the touring variety, which would bring art to a new public. And Daumier's friend Jeanron was, I believe, the man more responsible than anyone for founding the first Museum of Modern Art in the Luxembourg Palace.

Unfortunately for the painters, the government of the Second Republic grew quickly more and more reactionary, smoothing the way for Louis Napoleon's seizing of power and his subsequent proclamation as Emperor in December 1852. The functionaries with radical views were squeezed out, or forced to act carefully. When Jeanron commissioned a painting from Millet in 1848 no subject was set, and Millet painted the entirely secular *Haymakers Resting*, but when Daumier received a State commission after the Salon of 1849 he was asked to paint a religious picture, suitable for a church in the provinces.

This gave Daumier a great deal of trouble, and he appears to have tried out a number of possible subjects. There is in existence some correspondence between the painter and the Ministry of Fine Arts, and the matter was not settled until 1863 when the Ministry accepted *The Drunkenness of Silenus* (No. 5) in lieu of the religious picture.

One cannot be sure what Daumier's first idea was. He may have adapted the *Riot* composition, and produced the remarkable drawing in the Ashmolean (No. 102) which has long been known as *The Destruction of Sodom*, though it was perhaps entirely unconnected with this religious project and intended as an illustration for Henri Martin's *Histoire de France*. He may have painted a *Penitent Magdalen*; or he may have begun his largest canvas, called '*We want Barabbas*' (No. 2), which is hardly more than brushed in, but tremendously vivid; or he may have chosen *Christ and His Disciples* (No. 1), which has been taken very much further, and might even have been offered to and refused by the Commissioners.

The works connected with official commissions remained for the most part in the project stage, unseen except by those in Daumier's immediate circle. To the Salons of 1849 and 1850–51, however, he sent two large pictures that marked his public début as a painter. In 1849 he showed *The Miller, his Son and the Ass* (No. 7), with an unusual though not unknown subject from La Fontaine which would have been quite acceptable to nineteenth-century taste. The picture is also known as *The three Girls*, for obvious reasons, as Daumier was more concerned

10

to paint the three fleeing Rubensian nymphs, than to illustrate the fable. The girls reappeared in Daumier's painting for the next Salon, eighteen months later, *Two Nymphs pursued by Satyrs* (No. 6).

These pictures went almost unremarked at the Salons. None of the well-known critics like Champfleury, who for political reasons might have been expected to support their friend, came out in his support and one can only presume that they found Daumier's painting something of an embarrassment. It was so rough and crude in comparison with everything else in the Salons that even those well disposed towards Daumier and ready to praise his work as a lithographer and draughts-man preferred to pass it by in silence. It is perhaps worthy of note that neither of these works, nor the *Good Samaritan* in Glasgow, nor '*We want Barabbas*', was shown in the 1878 exhibition, though Daumier's four largest pictures were all in his possession at the time.

There is another thing that must have been painfully obvious to Daumier's artist friends, and that is the degree to which he was, as a painter, dependent on them for both subject and style. They were much more skilled than he was, in their knowledge both of how to paint and what to paint, and it was only natural that he should learn from them. To investigate such dependence is not to belittle Daumier, for it has nothing to do with the quality of the work, and any comparisons one makes are usually in his favour. It does however help to explain the reluctance of some of Daumier's contemporaries to accept him as a serious painter.

We know from a number of documents and the testimony of witnesses the artistic circle in which Daumier moved during the period 1847–55. It included the painters Daubigny, Diaz, Meissonier, Bonvin; the sculptors Préault and Geoffroy-Dechaume; and the critics Baude-laire and Champfleury. Most of them lived, like Daumier himself, on the Ile Saint-Louis, which was the St Germain-des-Prés of the time. Also friendly to Daumier, though not intimate, were Delacroix, Millet, Decamps, Courbet and Barye. The most influential, so far as Daumier's painting is concerned, were, in order of importance, Millet, Diaz, Decamps and, perhaps surprisingly, Meissonier.

Millet's work anticipates Daumier's in many respects, both in sub-ject and in style. Millet sustained a devotion to Michelangelo above all other artists from the moment that he first visited the Louvre in 1837, and a tendency to monumentalize the figure and set it against a neutral background appears quite early in his work. This would have immediately made his painting acceptable to Daumier who shared the worship of Michelangelo and had tried to do the same sort of thing in his early lithographs. Like Michelangelo too, Daumier was essentially a figure painter, and showed little interest in landscape or still life.

To a remarkable degree, Millet's paintings of 1845–50 foreshadow Daumier's subject matter. At that period Millet was famous for his undraped nymphs and fauns, but he also painted, in the words of Julia Cartwright, 'women bathing or resting under trees, children at play in flowery meadows, groups of youths and maidens dancing on the grass'. These are all Daumier subjects. Already in 1847–48 Millet was thinking of painting not only peasants like *The Winnower* and *The Sower*, but also the Parisian working class—stonemasons and navvies, a mother and child begging in the street, a drunken working man. Daumier was probably moving simultaneously in the same direction (cf. Nos. 77, 78) but the monumentalized figures of workers—the barge-tower, the man on a rope (Nos. 80, 81), and above all the washerwomen (Nos. 71–75)— all date from well after 1850. Millet, in fact, sent a painting of washerwomen to the Salon of 1850. He also made in the summer of 1849 pastels of horses drinking, and this was to become another Daumier subject (cf. Nos. 11–13). When he moved to Barbizon in 1849 Millet deliberately limited his range and set about realizing an idealized peasant existence, part biblical, part Virgilian. Had he stayed in Paris he would have become quite another painter. As it was, one might say that Daumier inherited his subjects, and because of his superior sense of form made them into paintings that today are more alive to us than most of Millet's work.

Daumier's connections with other painter friends are less fundamental and restricted mainly to common subject matter. It is not difficult to find parallels in contemporary French painting for such pictures as *Children coming out of School* (No. 20), *The first Bathe* (No. 9) and *Lunch in the Country* (No. 31). Clowns and acrobats were also popular, but Daumier was able in a work like *Les Saltimbanques* (in the Ionides Collection at the Victoria and Albert Museum) to lift the subject on to an altogether higher plane, and in doing so he anticipates Picasso. Perhaps in his old age Daumier compared himself to a clown. He would certainly have known Baudelaire's prose poem *Le vieux Saltimbanque* (1862) in which his friend uses the old clown as the symbol of an old poet, no longer celebrated; and one is aware in such works as the *Head of a Clown* (No. 67) of an element of self-portraiture.

Daumier again gives the subject a deeper meaning with *Refugees* (No. 15), a theme which obsessed him in the early 1850s and which he treated both in relief sculpture and in painting. The type of subject is not new—such long lines of figures on foot and on horseback spread out across the composition may be found in the paintings of Decamps and Meissonier and elsewhere. What is new is Daumier's treatment of it. No doubt it began as a descriptive picture of an actual event—probably the enforced emigrations after the 1848 revolution—but as Daumier continues to work at the subject he makes it less particular and more generalized in its sentiment. His first biographer, Alexandre, was tempted into an almost existentialist explanation which, though written in 1888, is still worth quoting at length:

'Daumier was more than once haunted by the idea of depicting the feeling of dread that man feels before the unknown, the melancholy and disquiet before leaving for unknown and distant places. Where are we going? What lot is reserved for us? On what shores are we going to land? Perhaps after a long and exhausting journey we shall find ourselves in impenetrable darkness. Perhaps, like slaves tied to the wheel, we shall make headway only to return to our point of departure. Such is the vague and disturbing question that comes to us before the two reliefs of the *Refugees*, which Daumier moulded in an hour of profound emotion. These are men with strong bodies, in the prime of life, women, and children with an unsteady step, who go in long lines in search of fortune, or in flight from some calamity.'

Daumier had reason for melancholy, because his attempt to make a name as a painter in the years immediately following the 1848 revolution met with complete failure. After the initial impetus had died out, he probably painted less and less, and after 1853, discouraged by the reception of his efforts, did not even send work to the Salon. During the 1850s he was producing lithographs at the rate of 100–150 a year, but the quality is on the whole lower than it was in the thirties and forties. We know that he hurried through his lithographic work so as to have time for painting, but making two or three cartoons a week must have been a steady drain on his imaginative resources. Even in 1858, when he was so ill that his friends thought he was going to die, Daumier made 127 plates.

The lithograph that appeared in *Le Charivari* for 1 March 1860 was however the last to appear in this journal for almost four years. The editor explained that M. Daumier wanted to devote himself to painting, but this may have been no more than a polite excuse. In fact Daumier seems to have been dismissed, presumably because of the decline in his work, and in the next four years he made only a few odd cartoons. In December 1863 *Le Charivari* announced his return, and from 1864 onwards, Daumier was again producing over 100 lithographs a year, and this rate was to last until his retirement due to failing eyesight in 1872.

It would seem reasonable to presume that a majority of Daumier's pictures were done in the years 1860–63, the only period of his life when he had the time to paint. The difficulties of making a chronological sequence of Daumier's paintings are, as Mr Maison points out in his illuminating notes on the paintings and drawings (p. 17), almost insuperable—not a picture is dated, and very few are datable; less than ten were publicly exhibited by Daumier during his working lifetime. Comparisons between paintings and lithographs are usually based on assumptions too hypothetical to be convincing. It is my belief that all one can hope to do at present—though the exhibition may well prove the contrary—is to make a very rough division of the existing paintings, according to style and subject-matter, into two groups, one centred on the years after 1848, and the other on the 'free' period 1860–63. The first group is more sculptural in style, the second more painterly—a tendency that reaches a climax in the very remarkable late works. In the earlier period come the more ambitious pictures with subjects chosen from religion, mythology, literature and contemporary history, together with some of the paintings of lawyers and the theatre scenes.

In the second period the subject-matter is almost entirely drawn from everyday life—people in the streets, in a railway carriage; people singing, drinking, eating, playing games; children dancing, talking, bathing, playing. Most of these paintings are small, the only exceptions being some of the washerwomen and the man on the rope, who is probably a *badigeonneur*—a man whitewashing. Daumier seems to have contemplated a series of working-class types; he also painted, admittedly on a much smaller scale, and sometimes only in water-colour, a man hauling a barge, a water-carrier, a rag-picker, a butcher and blacksmiths—a series that forms the urban counterpart to Millet's peasants.

Another very important class of Daumier's paintings in the 1860–63

14

period are the artists and collectors (Nos. 49–56). Unlike the working-class types, they have no political or social significance. One wonders why Daumier returned so often to this subject—twelve of the ninety-four oil paintings shown at the 1878 exhibition were of artists or collectors, and probably another dozen exist. The reason may be simple: they were relatively saleable. This was an extremely popular and well-established genre. Meissonier for example saw his *Painter at his Easel* sold at auction in 1861 for 11,200 francs and his *Amateurs de Peinture* went for 31,800 francs in 1868. (Daumier was paid forty francs for a lithograph and fifty for a water-colour.)

Iconographically Daumier and Meissonier have a great deal in common. This may seem surprising, but the two men were on friendly terms and Meissonier was the right person to tell Daumier how to make money out of painting. Before 1860 Meissonier had painted *Chess Players*, *Card Players*, *The Smoker*, *The Writer*, *A Man Reading*, *The Musician*, *A Painter showing his Drawings*, *The Amateurs*, *A Painter in his Studio*—and all these subjects were later taken up by Daumier. In style of course there is little similarity between the two men.

If the artists and collectors were painted in the hope of attracting purchasers, the Don Quixote pictures (Nos. 87–100) were done because the subject meant a great deal to Daumier. Cervantes's book was his favourite reading: he would have sympathized with Sancho's earthy realism, and to be ambitious and idealistic and meet only with disillusion was the fate both of Don Quixote and of Daumier himself.

Daumier sent a Don Quixote picture to the Salon of 1850; it was not a common subject, though Decamps had painted the Don charging windmills and Delacroix had shown him seated in his library. Daumier painted about twenty Don Quixote pictures, many of them after 1864 when he returned to lithography. He probably went on painting them until he began to go blind in 1873. The Courtauld picture (No. 97) for example is, I think, a very late work.

In his last years the ageing Daumier had still to struggle against poverty. He had left Paris: helped by the generosity of his friend Corot, in 1865 he moved to Valmondois, near Auvers, in the country outside Paris. As a painter he was no nearer to public success than he had ever been, and by now he was probably past caring. He would have found consolation in the steadfast support of old admirers like Daubigny and Dupré, and in the interest which his paintings were arousing among much younger artists. We have tantalizingly little certain knowledge about this, but one would conjecture for example that at some time in the sixties Cézanne and his friends asked Daumier to show them his work. In his paintings they would have discovered a sense of form, an awareness of light and shade, and a way of handling paint that could not but have excited them.

There is no parallel in the French art of the day for the extraordinary freedom of the late drawings and of paintings like the Courtauld *Don Quixote* (No. 97). Insubstantial figures and a wraith-like paint quality are also found in the *Woman carrying a Child* (No. 28) which is one of the last pictures that Daumier painted. It owes something to Fragonard, an important group of whose works came to the Louvre in 1869 with the Lacaze bequest, but as always Daumier transcends his models. We are aware of the painter's approaching blindness, but his work now seems lit up by a kind of inner illumination and a new visionary quality enters into it.

This is a quality that one finds only in the late works of the greatest masters—a Michelangelo or a Titian, a Rembrandt or a Cézanne. We cannot of course class Daumier with them, for in his case one has only the intimation of a late style, and not its rich achievement—here as elsewhere, his work as a painter is incomplete. It is however a measure of Daumier's greatness that his name can without incongruity be associated with theirs.

Daumier's Paintings and Drawings

by K. E. Maison

Not unlike Watteau, Daumier was undoubtedly aware of his mastery as a draughtsman, and at the same time he was too often dissatisfied with the quality of his painting. A considerable number of his pictures, even very sketchy ones, exist in several very similar versions; they are obviously proof of the artist's continuous effort to improve on his work. At the time of his death, many painted sketches and an assortment of unfinished pictures became the property of his widow who, in the course of the years, disposed of them. These sketches were in great numbers 'finished' by painters who sometimes knew the artist's style and technique very well. They are often not easily distinguishable from true originals, and even technical means such as infra-red light or X-rays are of little avail when the 'finishing' was done not so much later than the original work on a painting. Similarly, in some cases the artist proceeded with a composition a long way, only to leave it unfinished in the end because it did not satisfy him. The famous *Famille sur la Barricade* in Prague, where much important detail is surely not by Daumier, is one example; another is the big composition *The Good Samaritan* in Glasgow, a finished painting which, nearly ten years after the artist's death, was still described as a sketch.

Daumier frequently used his brush like a pencil: he drew with it on the panel or canvas which he had previously prepared with an even grounding (mostly in brown) and afterwards filled in more or less large areas with paint. His forgers, as well as the almost equally dishonest 'finishers' of his genuine sketches, often imitated this technique by painting a black surrounding line on the main details of a composition. However, the late David Rosen, an American restorer who gave much time and effort to the study of Daumier's technique of painting, went much too far when he came to regard scarcely any picture by the artist as authentic which did not show the drawing at least under infra-red light. Many authentic pictures are painted in a different technique.

Daumier as a *painter* was probably self-taught; there is at least no evidence of his having been any painter's pupil. His technical knowledge of the art of painting was consequently rather poor in the early stages and remained so for a very long time. Many of his pictures, especially those of before *c*. 1860, deteriorated badly and their restoration has often been a major operation, much dreaded by competent restorers. Various layers of oil glazes are often encountered, and the artist's frequent use of bitumen made matters worse still. In 1888, Daumier's earliest biographer, Arsène Alexandre, deplored this technique which had even then '*commencé à jouer à quelques-unes de ses toiles de déplorables tours*'; it often lead to the formation of the practically irreparable bitumen-craquelure, and almost invariably darkened the surface very seriously.

Some paintings have suffered so badly and are so extensively restored that they are no longer in a fit state to be shown in an exhibition; others are in such a delicate condition that removal and transport would have endangered them seriously, as for example the well-known *Amateurs de tableaux* in the collection of Mrs Harris Jonas, New York, or the two fine pictures representing painters in their studios, in the Musée des Beaux-Arts, Rheims.

However serious the question of the preservation of many of Daumier's paintings may be, the paramount problem facing the student is that of the authenticity of the works of this unusually widely imitated painter and draughtsman. It must certainly have been a unique experience for the artist to have himself discovered *un faux* in the show-window of an art shop in the rue de Seine. The forging of his works did not normally begin so early; during the first years of this century, however, quite a number of forgeries must already have been in circulation, paintings as well as drawings. A group of portraits erroneously attributed to Daumier were not forgeries, but were recently proved by H. Schwarz to be copies, by André Gill, after contemporary photographs. The portrait of Berlioz, lent to the 1901 Daumier exhibition at the Ecole des Beaux-Arts by the Versailles Museum, is perhaps the best-known example; other such portraits are of Dumas *père*, of Michelet, etc.

Prices obtained for Daumier's paintings began to rise steadily after the *Exposition Centennale* of 1889, and by the turn of the century, they had become sufficiently substantial to attract forgers in appreciable numbers. Several faked *Wagons de troisième classe* probably owe their existence to the fact that the main picture of that group (No. 69 in the present exhibition) fetched nearly Frs. 50.000 at the Doria Sale in 1899. Prices between Frs. 25.000 and Frs. 35.000 were repeatedly paid for small pictures by Daumier sold at Paris auctions in the first years of this century. Generally speaking, it appears that the majority of forgeries are relatively early; modern *pastiches* are rarer by far, and they are usually not very good.

Apart from pictures by unidentified painters, to which the initials *h.D.* had been added and which were passed off as being by Daumier, it appears that there are no Daumier forgeries which are free inventions. Several water-colours of railway subjects, drinkers, Court scenes and *amateurs* have repeatedly supplied forgers with material to work from. However, they very often made the basic mistake of producing more or less 'comic' pictures when their sources were satirical lithographs or woodcuts; they were unaware of the fact that the painter Daumier was neither a satirist nor a caricaturist, but—as one critic aptly expressed it —above all an observer of the usual.

There are scores of faked Daumier drawings which were copied from lithographs or woodcuts; while the extremely rare genuine sketches for some of the artist's graphic work are of course in the inverse direction of the final print, the imitations are not. The forgers generally selected one of the less-known prints and often used either pen and ink, or brush and brown ink for their *pastiches*, in most cases media which gave the drawings an appearance in some way different from the lithographs or woodcuts. Water-colour washes, applied to cover up too obvious weaknesses, are often met with, and frequently only part of the original composition is used for the fake. Although some spurious Daumier drawings can be traced back to the early years of the century (when their commercial value was truly negligible), the majority are of more recent date.

It will be noticed that the term 'signed' is avoided in this catalogue. Daumier usually signed his finished works, paintings as well as water-colours and wash drawings, either in full or with his monogram. The initials *h.D.* are very easy to imitate, and they were in fact frequently applied by a later hand to genuine unfinished pictures, or to sketches which the artist never signed. Genuine works with faked monograms are therefore not uncommon; this applies to paintings but almost more so to drawings. It appears that there are also a number of drawings executed at various times during Daumier's life which he signed later, sometimes perhaps even much later. To avoid prejudicing the authenticity of any of the works in this exhibition, it seemed preferable not to question the reliability of the signatures; where the signature *h. Daumier* appears in full on the paintings or drawings exhibited there can be no doubt of the authenticity of that signature, but it should by no means be assumed that the monogram *h.D.* was always added by a later hand.

As to the chronology of Daumier's paintings, it must be admitted that this problem is not yet satisfactorily solved. Although Jean Adhémar, of the Bibliothèque Nationale, Paris, has given much thought to this question and has arranged the reproductions in his book on Daumier in a sequence of a presumed chronology, this work was done to a great extent on the basis of photographs. Mr Oliver Larkin, of the Art Department of Smith College, Northampton (Mass.), has been studying the same problem for a long time; his conclusions, hitherto unpublished, appear to differ in many instances from those of Monsieur Adhémar. The latter's suggested dates for pictures exhibited here and reproduced in his book, are quoted in this catalogue. Further dates are suggested by the present writer, but these too should be regarded as hypothetical. It is to be hoped that this exhibition, which for the first time in sixty years unites so considerable a part of Daumier's painted *œuvre*, will be of help to students of the Master's art in their complicated task.

Catalogue

Catalogue Notes

Medium	All paintings are in oil unless otherwise stated.
Measurements	are in centimetres, followed by inches in brackets; the height is given first.
Inscriptions	(see p. 19) are given after the measurements. (L.l.=Lower left; U.l.=Upper left; L.l.c.=Lower left corner; L.r.=Lower right; U.r.=Upper right; L.r.c.=Lower right corner.)
Exhibitions	All exhibitions took place in London unless otherwise stated.

No reference is made to the exhibition of works once they have entered a public collection.

All abbreviated references, with the exceptions given below, apply to Daumier exhibitions only. Mixed exhibitions in private galleries are for the most part omitted.

The abbreviations used are self-explanatory, except for the following, which are used throughout this catalogue:

Albertina, 1936	*H. Daumier Ausstellung: Zeichnungen, Aquarelle, Lithographien und Kleinplastiken.* Vienna, Albertina, 1936.
Beaux-Arts, 1901	*Exposition Daumier.* Paris, Palais de l'Ecole des Beaux-Arts, 1901.
Bibliothèque Nationale, 1958	*Daumier: Le Peintre Graveur.* Paris, Bibliothèque Nationale, 1958.
Blot, 1908	*Exposition Daumier.* Paris, Galerie E. Blot, 1908.
Daumier-Gavarni, 1923	*Exposition Daumier—Gavarni.* Ville de Paris, Maison Victor Hugo, 1923.
Durand-Ruel, 1878	*Exposition des Peintures et Dessins de H. Daumier.* Paris, Galeries Durand-Ruel, 1878.
Galerie Dru, 1927	*Aquarelles et Dessins de Daumier.* Paris, Galerie L. Dru, 1927.
Galerie Rosenberg, 1907	*Exposition de Dessins, Aquarelles et Lithographies de H. Daumier.* Paris, Galerie L. & P. Rosenberg Fils, 1907.
La Caricature, 1888	*Exposition de Peintures, Aquarelles, Dessins et Lithographies de Maîtres Français de la Caricature et de la Peinture de Moeurs au XIXe siècle.* Paris, Ecole des Beaux-Arts, 1888. (Contained over sixty works by Daumier.)
Lefevre Galleries, 1922	*Drawings by H. Daumier* (from the Lemaire Collection, Paris). London, L. H. Lefevre & Son, 1922.

Lefevre Galleries, 1927	*Paintings and Drawings by Honoré Daumier.* London, Alex. Reid & Lefevre, 1927.
Leicester Galleries, 1936	*Paintings, Drawings and Lithographs by Honoré Daumier.* London, Leicester Galleries, 1936.
Matthiesen, 1926	*Ausstellung Honoré Daumier: Gemälde, Aquarelle und Zeichnungen.* Berlin, Galerie Matthiesen, 1926.
New York, 1930	*Corot—Daumier. Eighth Loan Exhibition.* New York, Museum of Modern Art, 1930.
Orangerie, 1934	*Daumier: Peintures, Aquarelles, Dessins.* Paris, Musée de l'Orangerie, 1934.
Philadelphia, 1937	*Daumier, 1808–1879.* Philadelphia, Pennsylvania Museum of Art, 1937. (The catalogue contains 'Technical Notes on Daumier' by D. Rosen and H. Marceau.)

Literature

Reference is made to all the principal monographs on the artist, but as the literature on Daumier is particularly extensive references to other publications have been restricted to a minimum.

Unless otherwise stated, the page references given apply only to illustrations, except in the case of the lists of the artist's works by Alexandre and Klossowski, where the first figure after the author's name represents the list number.

Unless otherwise stated, books and periodicals in English, French and German were published in London, Paris and Berlin respectively. (N.Y.=New York.)

The abbreviations used are self-explanatory except for the following, which are used throughout this catalogue:

Adhémar	Jean Adhémar, *Honoré Daumier*, Paris, 1954.
Adhémar *Drawings*	Jean Adhémar, *Honoré Daumier: Drawings and Watercolours* (English edition), New York and Basle, 1954.
Alexandre	Arsène Alexandre, *Honoré Daumier: L'Homme et l'Œuvre*, Paris, 1888.
Ars Graphica	*Les Dessins de Daumier. Introduction par Charles Baudelaire* (in the series *Ars Graphica*), Paris, 1949.
Cassou	Jean Cassou, *Daumier*, Lausanne, 1949.
Escholier, 1923	Raymond Escholier, *Daumier: Peintre et Lithographe* (in the series *La Vie et l'Art Romantiques*), Paris, 1923.
Escholier, 1930	Raymond Escholier, *Daumier*, Paris, 1930.
Escholier, 1938	Raymond Escholier, *Daumier* (in the series *Anciens et Modernes*), Paris, 1938.

Fleischmann/Sachs	Benno Fleischmann, *Honoré Daumier: Gemälde und Graphik*, Vienna, 1937. Maurice Sachs, *Honoré Daumier*, Paris, 1939 (French edition of the foregoing).
Fontainas	André Fontainas, *La Peinture de Daumier* (in the series *Ars Graphica*), Paris, 1923.
Fuchs	Eduard Fuchs, *Der Maler Daumier* (2nd edition, containing the Supplement), Munich, 1930.
Geffroy	Gustave Geffroy, *Daumier*, Paris, 1901. (Reprint of an article in *Revue de l'Art Ancien et Moderne*, vol. IX.)
Kalitina	N. Kalitina, *Honoré Daumier*, Moscow, 1955. (Text in Russian.)
Klossowski	Erich Klossowski, *Honoré Daumier* (2nd edition), Munich, 1923.
Lassaigne	Jacques Lassaigne, *Daumier*, Paris (Hyperion), 1938.
Lassaigne, 1946	Jacques Lassaigne, *Daumier* (in the series *Les Grands Maîtres de la Peinture*), Paris, 1946.
Maison, in *Burl. Mag.*	K. E. Maison, 'Daumier Studies', in *The Burlington Magazine*, January, March and April 1954, and May and June 1956.
Maison *Drawings*	K. E. Maison, *Daumier Drawings*, New York and London, 1960.
Martine-Marotte	*Honoré Daumier, Cinquante Réproductions* (in facsimile) *de Léon Marotte, avec un catalogue par Charles Martine*, Paris, 1924.
Sadleir	Michael Sadleir, *Daumier: The Man and the Artist*, London, 1924.
Scheiwiller	Giovanni Scheiwiller, *Honoré Daumier* (in the series *Arte Moderna Straniera*), Milan, 1936.
Schweicher	Curt Schweicher, *Daumier* (in the series *Ars Mundi*), London, 1954.
Ziller	Gerhart Ziller, *Honoré Daumier*, Dresden, 1957.

Catalogue

Paintings

1 Christ and His Disciples

*Jésus et ses disciples—Le Christ instruisant
ses disciples*

Canvas: 65 by 81 (25⅝ by 31⅞). L.r.c.: *h.D.*

PROVENANCE: van Lijnden.

LITERATURE: Klossowski, 80 and pl. 64; Fuchs,
152; Adhémar, pl. 48 ('*vers* 1850').

*Lent by the Rijksmuseum, Amsterdam (on loan to the
Stedelijk Museum)*

One of several studies painted by Daumier in the
hope of obtaining a commission for a painting from
the Government. This ambition, however, was not
satisfied, but in 1863 the Commission des Beaux-
Arts acquired from the artist the *Marche de Silène*,
now at Calais (see No. 5).

2 'We want Barabbas!'

*Nous voulons Barabbas!—Jésus et Barab-
bas—Ecce Homo*   PLATE I

Grisaille on canvas: 160 by 127 (63 by 50).

PROVENANCE: Mme Daumier; Diot; Vollard;
Osthaus.

LITERATURE: Alexandre, p. 373; *Kunst und
Künstler*, XII, 1914, p. 252; Klossowski, 81 and
pl. 65; Sadleir, pl. 56; Fuchs, 149; Scheiwiller,
pl. VII; R. Lejeune, *Daumier*, Zürich, 1945, pl.
194; Cassou, pl. 53; Adhémar, pl. 49 ('*vers* 1850');
Schweicher, repr. in text, p. xx.

Lent by the Museum Folkwang, Essen

The difficulty in dating many of Daumier's works is
clearly demonstrated by the fact that, even in the
case of so important a painting as this, two authors
of repute suggest greatly differing dates: while
M. Adhémar places the picture around 1850,
M. Cassou believes it to be *une œuvre de la fin*,
i.e. towards 1870, before the artist's eyesight began
to fail.

3 Oedipus and the Shepherd

Oedipe et le berger   PLATE 22B

Canvas: 65 by 50 (25⅝ by 19¾). L.r.c.: *h.D.*

PROVENANCE: Boy; Zierer; Cassirer; Jungers;
Tanner; Lewin; Silberberg.

EXHIBITIONS: Paris, *Exposition Centennale*, 1900
(178); *Daumier-Gavarni*, 1923 (12); Matthiesen, 1926
(68); Zürich, Kunsthaus, *Französische Maler des
XIX. Jahrhunderts*, 1933 (33); Orangerie, 1934 (2);
Leicester Galleries, 1936 (92).

LITERATURE: *Cat. de la Vente Boy*, Paris, 1904, No.
10, and 1905, No. 6; Klossowski, 3 and pl. 18; *Cahiers
d'Art*, III, 1928, p. 190; Fuchs, 146; *Cat. de la
Vente Silberberg*, Paris, 1932, No. 19; Fleischmann/
Sachs, pl. 2; Lassaigne, pl. 119; C. Roger-Marx,
Daumier, Paris, 1938, p. 52; Adhémar, pl. 50
('1849/50').

Lent by Mr Justin K. Thannhauser, New York

According to legend, the newly born Oedipus was
exposed by his father, Laius, but was found by a
shepherd of Polybus, king of Corinth, who adopted
him. Millet exhibited a painting of the same subject
at the Salon of 1847 which very possibly inspired
Daumier to paint this picture.

4 Silenus and two Satyrs   PLATE 22A

Silène et deux faunes—Faunes et satyres

Panel: 16 by 22 (6⅜ by 8⅝). L.l.c.: *h.D.*

PROVENANCE: Arosa; H. Rouart; Vollard; Dr A.
Hahnloser.

EXHIBITIONS: Winterthur, Kunstmuseum, *Meisterwerke aus Privatsammlungen*, 1922 (30); Cannes,
Musée, *La Provence et ses peintres au XIXᵉ siècle*,
1929 (13); Lucerne, Kunstmuseum, *Die Hauptwerke
der Sammlung Hahnloser*, 1940 (37).

LITERATURE: *Cat. de la Vente G. Arosa*, Paris, 1878,
No. 27; Alexandre, p. 374; *Cat. de la Vente H.
Rouart*, Paris, 1912, I, No. 167; Klossowski, 15 and
pl. 29; Fuchs, 145b.

Lent by Professor Dr Hans R. Hahnloser, Berne

5 The Drunkenness of Silenus

L'ivresse de Silène—La marche de Silène

Black chalk, charcoal and gouache: 43 by 61 (17 by 24). L.l.: *h. Daumier*.

PROVENANCE: Acquired from the artist by the State in 1863; transferred to Calais in 1868.

EXHIBITION: Paris, Salon, 1850 (728).

LITERATURE: J. and E. Goncourt, in *Le Temps, Illustrateur Universel*, 3, 1860, accompanied by a woodcut reproduction (by Trichon); Roger Marx, *Les Maîtres de Dessin*, 1900, pl. 49; Klossowski, 12 and pl. 18; Martine-Marotte, pl. 1; Fuchs, 266b; C. Roger-Marx, *Daumier*, 1938, p. 53; Escholier, 1938, p. 81; Adhémar, *Drawings*, pl. 6; Adhémar, pl. 58 ('1850'); Kalitina, pl. 70.

Lent by the Musée des Beaux-Arts, Calais

Many details of this composition are borrowed from Rubens's picture of the same subject, now in the National Gallery, London. As the original had left France in 1830, Daumier must have based his drawing on the engraving by Delauney which, being in the inverse sense of the original, reproduces the picture in the same direction as Daumier used it. There are striking resemblances between the composition of the three young women in the painting *The Miller, his Son and the Ass* (see No. 7) and the three female figures in the present picture.

6 Two Nymphs pursued by Satyrs

*Deux nymphes poursuivies par des satyres
—Bacchantes* PLATE 3

Canvas: 131·5 by 97·2 (51⅝ by 38¼). L.r.c.: *h.D.*

PROVENANCE: Wisselingh; Sir William van Horne; Adaline van Horne.

EXHIBITION: Paris, Salon, 1850 (726).

LITERATURE: Alexandre, p. 373; Klossowski, 17 and pl. 25; Fuchs, 143b; *Art News* (N.Y.), 15 February 1942, p. 22; Adhémar, pl. 56, in colour ('1849/50').

Lent by the Montreal Museum of Fine Arts, Bequest of Miss Adaline Van Horne

This picture was without doubt painted expressly for exhibition at the Salon. See note on No. 7.

7 The Miller, his Son and the Ass

Le Meunier, son fils et l'âne PLATE 2

Canvas: 130 by 97 (51⅛ by 38¼). L.r.c.: *h. Daumier*.

PROVENANCE: Bignou; Wisselingh; Col. Woods; Reid & Lefevre.

EXHIBITIONS: Paris, Salon, 1849 (484); Lefevre Galleries, 1927 (2); Arts Council travelling exhibition, 1950, *French Paintings of the 19th Century from the Burrell Collection* (18).

LITERATURE: *L'Artiste*, 1849, p. 113; Alexandre, p. 373; Klossowski, 4; Fuchs, 142; L. Venturi, *Peintres Modernes*, N.Y., 1941, p. 183; D. Talbot Rice, in *Scottish Art Review* (Glasgow), 3, 1946, p. 2; *Art News* (N.Y.), October 1944, p. 16, and 1949, p. 42; Cassou, pl. 49; Adhémar, pl. 62, in colour ('1849'); Kalitina, plate facing p. 113.

Lent by the Corporation of Glasgow, Burrell Collection

Daumier painted this scene for exhibition at the Salon. At a time when the great majority of pictures shown there were 'telling a story', he may well have chosen a literary theme to make his work acceptable to the dreaded Jury. It is obvious that it was not the La Fontaine fable which interested him most, but the composition of the three gay young women dominating the picture. This also applies to the *Two Nymphs pursued by Satyrs* shown at the Salon of the following year (see No. 6). A much smaller version is in the Gerstenberg Collection, while the Barnes Foundation, Merion (Pa.), owns a painted study of the same dimensions as the present picture.

8 The Bathers PLATE 23B

La baignade—Baigneurs—Avant le bain

Panel: 25 by 32 (9⅞ by 12⅜).

PROVENANCE: M. . . (?); Feydeau; Hazard; A. Reid; Gow; Reid & Lefevre.

EXHIBITIONS: Durand-Ruel, 1878 (89); Beaux-Arts, 1901 (468); Kirkcaldy, Art Gallery, Inaugural Loan Exhibition, 1925 (13); Lefevre Galleries, 1927 (7); Arts Council travelling exhibition, *Paintings from the Burrell Collection*, 1947 (2); Arts Council travelling exhibition, *French Paintings of the 19th Century from the Burrell Collection*, 1950 (17).

LITERATURE: Alexandre, p. 375; *Cat. de la Vente M. . .*, Paris, 29 April 1899, No. 5; *Cat. de la Vente Feydeau*, Paris, 1901, No. 43; *Cat. de la Vente Hazard*, Paris, 1919, No. 94; Klossowski, 282; Fuchs, 289a; A. Bertram, *Honoré Daumier* (in 'World's Masters' series), 1929, pl. 12; *Cahiers d'Art*, 1931, 3, p. 123; Adhémar, pl. 71, in colour ('vers 1852').

Lent by the Corporation of Glasgow, Burrell Collection

An upright study of the same subject is in a private collection in Paris.

9 The first Bathe

Le premier bain PLATE 22G

Panel: 15 by 23 (5⅞ by 9). L.r.c.: *h.D.*

PROVENANCE: Esnault-Pelterie; R. Lagrave; Knoedler.

Lent by Mr James E. Hanson, London

Probably painted as early as 1850–53. An unrecorded study for the larger painting in the collection of Mr Robert H. Tannahill, Grosse Point Farms (Mich.). Several studies, some of them of doubtful authenticity, are known for this and a closely related composition (in the collection of Dr Oskar Reinhart, Winterthur).

10 Young Girls bathing

Le bain des jeunes filles—Baigneuses—Au bord de l'eau PLATE 4

Panel: 33 by 24 (13 by 9½). L.l.c.: *h.D.*

PROVENANCE: Durand-Ruel; Hazard; Schoeller; Cognacq.

EXHIBITIONS: Durand-Ruel, 1878 (73); Beaux-Arts, 1901 (469); Lefevre Galleries, 1927 (7); Orangerie, 1934 (14); Paris, Palais National des Arts, *Chefs d'œuvre de l'Art français*, 1937 (155); Amsterdam, Stedelijk Museum, *Honderd Jaar Fransche Kunst*, 1938 (84); Travelling exhibition, Montevideo, Buenos Aires and Rio de Janeiro, *Art français*, 1939; New York, Metropolitan Museum, *De David à Toulouse-Lautrec*, 1941 (25 A); Bibliothèque Nationale, 1958 (316).

LITERATURE: Alexandre, p. 374; *Cat. de la Vente Hazard*, Paris, 1919, No. 95; Klossowski, 281; Fontainas, pl. 43; Escholier, 1923, plate facing p. 48, and 1938, p. 25, in colour; Fuchs, 56; Fleischmann/Sachs, pl. 88; Lassaigne, pl. 103; *Cat. de la Vente G. Cognacq*, Paris, 1952, No. 36; Adhémar, pl. 78, in colour ('1858/60'); Schweicher, pl. V, in colour; Kalitina, pl. 63; Ziller, pl. 94.

Lent by Monsieur Pierre Lévy, Troyes

11 The Watering-place PLATE 6A

L'abreuvoir—Au Bords de la Seine

Panel: 44·5 by 54·6 (17½ by 21½). L.r.c.: *h.D.*

PROVENANCE: Alexandre (?); T. G. Arthur; Colnaghi.

EXHIBITIONS: Durand-Ruel, 1878 (81); Glasgow, International Exhibition, 1901 (1356); Leicester Galleries, 1936 (86); Cardiff/Swansea, Arts Council exhibition, *Daumier, Millet, Courbet*, 1957 (6).

LITERATURE: Cat. of the T. G. Arthur Sale, London, 1914, No. 88; Klossowski, 34B; Fuchs, 294; Lassaigne, pl. 114; Adhémar, pl. 109 ('1860/ 2'); Schweicher, pl. 35.

Lent by Miss Margaret S. Davies, Montgomeryshire

Daumier moved into his studio on the Quai d'Anjou in about 1845 and stayed there until 1863. Several paintings depicting horses being taken to their watering place bear witness to the interest Daumier took in the artistic possibilities of this scene which he must have witnessed hundreds of times. These pictures are difficult to date; the example here shown appears to be not later than 1850–55.

12 Bather at the Watering-place

Baignade—L'abreuvoir PLATE 6B

Panel: 28·5 by 36·8 (11¼ by 14½). L.r.c.: *h.D.*

PROVENANCE: Camentron; Goupil Gallery; Margaret S. Davies; Agnew.

EXHIBITIONS: Durand-Ruel, 1878 (80); Leicester Galleries, 1936 (91).

LITERATURE: Klossowski, 32 (without details); Maison, in *Gazette des Beaux-Arts*, May/June, 1958, p. 345 and Fig. 5; Cat. of a Sale at Sotheby's, London, 4 May 1960, No. 108.

Lent by Lord Wharton

Painted about 1855.

13 The Horsemen PLATE 6D

Les cavaliers—Chevaux à l'abreuvoir

Canvas: 65 by 85 (25⅝ by 33½).

PROVENANCE: Blot; Durand-Ruel; Harrison Tweed.

EXHIBITIONS: Beaux-Arts, 1901 (13); Blot, 1908 (16); New York, 1930 (56).

LITERATURE: *Cat. de la Vente Blot*, Paris, 1900, No. 29, and 1906, No. 22; Klossowski, 33 and pl. 32; Fontainas, pl. 44; Fuchs, 83; Lassaigne, pl. 115; R. Lejeune, *Daumier*, 1945, pl. 192; Adhémar, pl. 107 ('vers 1861').

Lent by the Museum of Fine Arts, Boston, Mass.

Perhaps datable as early as 1850. Various studies, in charcoal or pen, as well as in oil, are connected with this composition.

14 Horsemen in a Wood

Cavaliers dans la forêt PLATE 6C

Canvas: 25·5 by 44·7 (10 by 17⅝).

PROVENANCE: Durand-Ruel; Wisselingh.

LITERATURE: Fuchs, 153; Lassaigne, pl. 116; Adhémar, pl. 43 ('*vers* 1848').

Lent from a Private Collection, The Netherlands

15 Refugees PLATE 22 I

Les fugitifs—Les émigrants—Une fuite

Panel: 16·2 by 28·7 (6⅜ by 11¼).

PROVENANCE: Mme Bernard-Léon; Camentron; Boulanger; Musée Carnavalet.

EXHIBITION: Durand-Ruel, 1878 (65).

LITERATURE: Alexandre, p. 374; Klossowski, 23; C. Roger-Marx, *Daumier*, Paris, 1938, p. 39; Escholier, 1938, p. 43, in colour; Lassaigne, pl. 113, in colour; Lassaigne, 1946, p. 41, in colour; Schweicher, pl. IV, in colour.

Lent by the Musée du Petit Palais, Paris

The subject of this painting is one that fascinated Daumier over a period of many years. The several painted versions which exist are, however, very different from each other in conception, style and size; the well-known relief *Les Emigrants*, repeatedly cast in bronze, belongs of course to the same group. The date of the present picture is presumably 1850–55.

16 The Rescue

Le sauvetage PLATE 8A

Canvas: 35 by 28 (13¾ by 11).

PROVENANCE: Camentron; Blot; Druet; Holzmann; Tanner; Bernheim Jeune; P. M. Turner; S. Courtauld.

EXHIBITIONS: Beaux-Arts, 1901 (27); Blot, 1908 (9); Matthiesen, 1926 (52?); New York, 1930 (82); London, Tate Gallery, *Samuel Courtauld Memorial Exhibition*, 1948 (19); Cardiff/Swansea, Arts Council exhibition, *Daumier, Millet, Courbet*, 1957 (8).

LITERATURE: *Cat. de la Vente E. Blot*, Paris, 1906, No. 23; Klossowski, 316 and pl. 134; Fuchs, 65; Lassaigne, pl. 102; D. Cooper, Cat. of the Courtauld Collection, 1954, No. 19 and pl. 2; Adhémar, pl. 120 ('1860/62').

Lent by Christabel, Lady Aberconway, London and North Wales

Although Daumier appears to have been much

preoccupied by this composition, no finished version of it is known. The present study might have been painted as late as 1865–68.

17 The Rescue

Le sauvetage PLATE 22H

Canvas: 15·5 by 24 (6⅛ by 9½). L.r.: *h.D.*

PROVENANCE: Tanner; Bernheim Jeune.

EXHIBITION: Matthiesen, 1926 (46).

LITERATURE: Fuchs, 64a.

Lent by Mr Joseph H. Hazen, New York

18 The Kiss PLATE 8B

Le baiser—Un homme et son enfant

Panel: 37 by 28 (14⅝ by 11). L.l.c.: *H.D.*

PROVENANCE: Lavoignat; Forbes; Eissler; Weiss.

EXHIBITIONS: Durand-Ruel, 1878 (22); New York, 1930 (89); Orangerie, 1934 (16).

LITERATURE: Alexandre, p. 375; *Kat. der Sammlung J. S. Forbes*, Munich, 1906, II, No. 28 (as *Nach der Arbeit*); Klossowski, 317 and pl. 108; Fuchs, 69; Adhémar, pl. 122 ('*vers* 1861').

Lent through the courtesy of the Musée des Beaux-Arts, Berne

Perhaps not later than 1850–53. Another version, of approximately the same size on an oblong canvas, depicts the same scene with the Pont-Neuf in the background (present whereabouts unknown).

19 Group of Women and Children

Femmes et enfants—La Causette PLATE 9A

Panel: 32 by 18 (12⅝ by 7⅛). L.l.c.: *h.D.*

PROVENANCE: Mesdag.

LITERATURE: Klossowski, 327; Fuchs, 66; Adhémar, pl. 64 ('*vers* 1850–1860').

Lent by the Rijksmuseum H. W. Mesdag, The Hague

20 Children coming out of School

La sortie—La sortie de l'école PLATE 9C

Panel: 40 by 31 (15¾ by 12¼). L.l.c.: *h. Daumier.*

PROVENANCE: Doria; Mante; Lutz; Jaubert; Hirsch; Chaine & Simonson; Matthiesen; Wildenstein; Renand.

EXHIBITIONS: Durand-Ruel, 1878 (85); Matthiesen, 1926 (43); Orangerie, 1934 (16a); Paris, Palais National des Arts, *Chefs d'œuvre de l'Art français*, 1937 (287); Bibliothèque Nationale, 1958 (170).

LITERATURE: Alexandre, p. 375; *Cat. de la Vente Comte A. Doria*, Paris, 1899, No. 130; Geffroy, p. 9; *Cat. de la Vente G. Lutz*, Paris, 1902, No. 48; *Cat. de la Vente Hirsch*, Paris, 1912, No. 14; Klossowski, 319; Fontainas, pl. 32; Escholier, 1923, p. 47, 1930, pl. 22, and 1938, p. 79, in colour; Fuchs, 67; Fleischmann/Sachs, pl. 78; Lassaigne, pl. 89, in colour; Lassaigne, 1946, p. 19, in colour; Adhémar, pl. 74, in colour ('1853/55'); Schweicher, pl. I, in colour; Ziller, pl. 101.

Lent by Monsieur Alfred Daber, Paris

21 Children Playing

Enfants jouant

Panel: 33·6 by 43·2 (13¼ by 17). L.r.c.: *h. Daumier.*

PROVENANCE: Maria Slavona; Stahl; J. B. Neumann.

EXHIBITION: Matthiesen, 1926 (32).

LITERATURE: Klossowski, 328 and pl. 136; Fuchs, 51b.

Lent by the World House Galleries, New York

22 Children under a Tree

Groupe d'enfants sous un arbre—Contes de fées PLATE 9B

Canvas: 55·5 by 47 (21⅞ by 18½). L.l.c.: *h.D.*

PROVENANCE: Dr de Saint-Germain; Katzenellenbogen.

EXHIBITIONS: Beaux-Arts, 1901 (60); Basle, Société des Beaux-Arts, *Peinture française*, 1921 (56); *Daumier-Gavarni*, 1923 (22); Matthiesen, 1926 (64); Zürich, Kunsthaus, *Französische Maler des XIX. Jahrhunderts*, 1933 (32).

LITERATURE: Klossowski, 323 and 324 and pl. 132; Fuchs, 54a; *Art Digest* (N.Y.), 1 February 1937, p. 10; *Art News* (N.Y.), 18 September 1937, p. 18.

Lent by the Toledo Museum of Art, Ohio

Painted about 1850–54.

23 Girl with a small Child

Jeune fille et enfant—Les petites paysannes

Canvas: 54·5 by 62·8 (21½ by 24⅜). L.l.c.: *h.D.*

PROVENANCE: P. Rosenberg; Gérard.

EXHIBITION: Wolfsburg, Stadthalle, *Französische Malerei: von Delacroix bis Picasso*, 1961 (37).

LITERATURE: Lassaigne, pl. 105, in colour; *Apollo*, 1939, p. 306; Lassaigne, 1946, p. 31, in colour; Schweicher, pl. 40; Adhémar, pl. 77 (with references not relating to this painting. '1852/6'); Cat. of a Sale at Sotheby's, 26 March 1958, No. 150.

Lent from a Private Collection

24 Heads of two Children

Têtes d'enfants

Panel: 22 by 27·5 (8⅝ by 10⅞). L.r.c.: *H.D.*

PROVENANCE: Leroy; Tempelaere; Groesbeck; Wisselingh.

LITERATURE: Maison, in *Gazette des Beaux-Arts*, May/June 1958, p. 342, Fig. 2.

Lent from a Private Collection, The Netherlands

This fairly late sketch is one of twelve which the firm of Tempelaere bought in 1895 from a Monsieur Leroy in Versailles.

25 Portrait of a Woman

Buste de femme—La Commère PLATE 10A

Canvas: 41 by 32·5 (16⅛ by 12¾).

PROVENANCE: Hazard; Barbazanges; Reid & Lefevre; McInnes.

EXHIBITIONS: Lefevre Galleries, 1927 (12); Glasgow, Art Gallery, *The Spirit of France*, 1943 (18).

LITERATURE: *Cat. de la Vente Hazard*, Paris, 1919, No. 102; Klossowski, 297; Fuchs, 3.

Lent by Glasgow Art Gallery and Museum

26 Head of an old Woman

Tête de vieille femme

Panel: 22 by 16·5 (8⅝ by 6½).

PROVENANCE: Vollard; Leo and Gertrude Stein; J. M. Price.

LITERATURE: Fuchs, 15a.

Lent by the Henry Pearlman Foundation, New York

This little study, probably dating from the later 1850s, was one of the first two pictures the Steins bought from Vollard (in 1901 or 1904). A repeatedly reproduced photograph of 1910, of their studio at 27 rue de Fleurus, shows this picture hanging in a group with Picasso's portrait of Gertrude Stein. The original photograph is in the Yale University Library (Stein Collection).

27 Woman wearing a blue Ribbon

La femme au ruban bleu—Buste de femme
PLATE 10B

Canvas: 40 by 32 (15¾ by 12⅝). R.u.c.: *h.D.*

PROVENANCE: Mirbeau; Kelekian.

EXHIBITION: Philadelphia, 1937 (14).

LITERATURE: *Cat. de la Vente O. Mirbeau*, Paris, 1919, No. 16; Cat. of the Kelekian Collection, New York, 1920, pl. 23; *Burl. Mag.*, Dec. 1920, pl. IIB; Cat. of the D. Kelekian Sale, New York, 1922, No. 102; Klossowski, 294 and pl. 131; Fuchs, 10; Lassaigne, pl. 38.

Lent by the Dumbarton Oaks Collection, Washington

Painted about 1850. A radiograph made at the Philadelphia Museum of Art (reproduced in the catalogue of the 1937 exhibition, fig. x) shows previous use of the canvas for a horizontal composition, probably a *Loge de théâtre*.

28 Woman carrying a Child

Femme portant un enfant
PLATE 9D

Canvas: 40·5 by 32·5 (15⅞ by 12¾). L.l.c.: *h.D.*

PROVENANCE: Dechaume; Viau; Fuchs; Wildenstein.

EXHIBITIONS: Beaux-Arts, 1901 (290); New York, 1930 (84); Paris, Orangerie, *Monticelli et le Baroque Provençal*, 1953 (26); Zürich, Kunsthaus, *Sammlung Emil G. Bührle*, 1958 (128).

LITERATURE: Klossowski, 299; *Cahiers d'Art*, III, 1928, p. 191; Fuchs, 59; Adhémar, pl. 174 ('*vers 1869*'); *Atlantis* (Zürich), 1955, Fig. 101; *Kat. Sammlung Emil G. Bührle*, Zürich, 1958, No. 128.

Lent from a Private Collection, Zürich

Presumably one of the very latest painted studies by Daumier.

29 The Secret

La Confidence
PLATE 8C

Canvas: 26 by 35 (10¼ by 13¾). L.u.c.: *h.D.*

PROVENANCE: Blot; H. Nathan (Frankfurt); Mme Nathan (Geneva).

EXHIBITIONS: Beaux-Arts, 1901 (12); Blot, 1908 (13); Leicester Galleries, 1936 (95).

LITERATURE: Geffroy, p. 20; *Kunst und Künstler*, XV (1917), p. 108; Klossowski, 296 and pl. 121; Fuchs, 130; Lassaigne, pl. 91; Adhémar, pl. 144 ('*vers 1860*').

Lent by Monsieur Leonard C. Stein, Geneva

30 The Beer Drinkers

Les buveurs de bière—Le fumeur
PLATE 7C

Panel: 22·5 by 27 (8⅞ by 10⅝). L.l.c.: *h. Daumier.*

PROVENANCE: Salomon (?); Esnault-Pelterie.

EXHIBITIONS: Durand-Ruel, 1878 (90)(?); Paris, Galerie Georges Petit, *Chefs d'œuvre de l'Ecole française*, 1910 (48); Orangerie, 1934 (8); Philadelphia, 1937 (4); Paris, Petit Palais, '*De Géricault à Matisse*', Chefs d'œuvre français des Collections Suisses, 1959 (37).

LITERATURE: Alexandre, p. 375(?); Klossowski, 272; Fontainas, pl. 18; Fuchs, 35b; Fleischmann/ Sachs, pl. 84; Lassaigne, pl. 42; *Formes et Couleurs*, 1945, III/IV, p. 381; Schweicher, pl. 8.

Lent by Dr Fritz Nathan, Zürich

Painted about 1855–60.

31 Lunch in the Country

Le déjeuner à la campagne—Fin d'un déjeuner
PLATE 7D

Panel: 25·5 by 33·5 (10 by 13⅛).

PROVENANCE: Lemaire; Bernheim Jeune; Gwendoline E. Davies.

EXHIBITIONS: Durand-Ruel, 1878 (10); *La Caricature*, 1888 (367); Beaux-Arts, 1901 (50); Bath, Victoria Art Gallery, 1918; Aberystwyth, National Library of Wales, 1946.

LITERATURE: Alexandre, p. 375; W. G. Constable, in *Burl. Mag.*, February 1920, p. 93; Klossowski, 268 and 268B; Maison, in *Apollo*, July/August 1952, Fig. II; Maison, in *Burl. Mag.*, April 1954, No. 3 and Fig. 12.

Lent by the National Museum of Wales, Cardiff

Painted about 1860. A painted sketch for this composition, of approximately the same size, is in the collection of Dr Oskar Reinhart, Winterthur.

32 The Drunkards

Les ivrognes—Le départ du Café

Peinture à l'essence on paper: 24·5 by 26·2 (9⅝ by 10⅜).

PROVENANCE: Lemaire; C. Roger-Marx.

EXHIBITIONS: Lefevre Galleries, 1922 (12); Galerie Dru, 1927 (47); New York, 1930 (108); Orangerie, 1934 (9); Albertina, 1936 (56); Leicester Galleries, 1936 (9); Philadelphia, 1937 (15).

LITERATURE: Klossowski, 265B (described as a

sanguine drawing); Fuchs, p. 52, Fig. 79 (described as a pen and sepia drawing).

Lent by Monsieur Roger Leybold, Paris

Probably an early sketch, before 1840, it is one of the artist's very few works in this technique.

33 Billiard-players

Joueurs de billard PLATE 7A

Panel: 22 by 27 (8⅝ by 10⅝). L.l.c.: *h.D.*

PROVENANCE: Alexandre; Gérard; Benatov.

EXHIBITIONS: Paris, Musée Carnavalet, *Chefs d'œuvre des Collections Parisiennes*, 1952 (29).

LITERATURE: *Cat. de la Vente Arsène Alexandre*, Paris, 1903, No. 22; Klossowski, 354.

Lent from a Private Collection

Daumier drew a series of thirteen caricatures of billiard-players for the *Journal Amusant*, published early in 1865. Possibly the subject as such attracted him at the time, although this date seems somewhat late for the painting shown here.

34 The Chess-players

Les joueurs d'échecs PLATE 7B

Panel: 24·5 by 32·5 (9⅝ by 12¾). L.l.c.: *h.Daumier.*

PROVENANCE: Jacquette.

LITERATURE: Klossowski, 350; Fontainas, pl. 17; Escholier, 1923, p. 138, and 1930, pl. 38; Sadleir, pl. 51; Fuchs, 36; *Commemorative Cat. of the Exhibition of French Art at the Royal Academy, 1932*, 1933, No. 325; Fleischmann/Sachs, pl. 81; Lassaigne, pl. 41; *Formes et Couleurs*, 1945, III/IV, p. 382; Lassaigne, 1946, p. 13, in colour; Cassou, pl. 36, in colour; Adhémar, pl. 145, in colour ('*vers* 1863'); Schweicher, pl. 9.

Lent by the Musée du Petit Palais, Paris

This picture has been exhibited frequently since it entered the possession of the Petit Palais. A painting identical in subject and size is in the J. K. Thannhauser Collection, New York.

35 The Reading

La lecture PLATE 22D

Panel: 27 by 35 (10⅝ by 13¾). L.r.c.: *h. Daumier.*

PROVENANCE: Wisselingh; Reich.

LITERATURE: Fuchs, 29b.

Lent by the Rijksmuseum, Amsterdam (on loan to the Stedelijk Museum)

Probably dates from the mid-1850s. A closely related painting is in the Gerstenberg Collection (see also No. 36).

36 A Man reading, with a small Boy

Un homme lisant, et un petit garçon—La lecture

Panel: 22 by 28 (8⅝ by 11).

PROVENANCE: Fabbri; G. Bernheim; Juan Girondo.

EXHIBITION: Beaux-Arts, 1901 (40).

LITERATURE: Klossowski, 347.

Lent by the Museo Nacional de Bellas Artes, Buenos Aires

The picture supposedly represents Georges Feydeau as a boy, with his father reading to him.

37 The Reader

Le Liseur PLATE 22F

Panel: 25·5 by 32·5 (10 by 12¾). L.l.: *h.D.*

PROVENANCE: Doria; E. Richard-Bühler; P. Rosenberg.

EXHIBITIONS: Basle, Société des Beaux-Arts, *Peinture Française*, 1921 (57); Leicester Galleries, 1936 (93).

LITERATURE: *Cat. de la Vente Comte A. Doria*, Paris, 1899, No. 135; Klossowski, 353; Fuchs, 28a.

Lent by Mr Justin K. Thannhauser, New York

Painted about 1850–55.

38 A Writer

Un écrivain—La rédaction du placet—Le manuscrit—Au travail—Le dessinateur [?]—La leçon de peinture [?] PLATE 11C

Panel: 25 by 33 (9⅞ by 13). L.l.c.: *h. Daumier.*

PROVENANCE: Dollfus; Mancini; Schmitz.

EXHIBITIONS: Durand-Ruel, 1878 (93); Paris, Louvre, *Exposition de tableaux, statues et objets d'art au profit de l'œuvre des orphelins de l'Alsace Lorraine*, 1885 (103?); Zürich, Kunsthaus, *Die Sammlung Oscar Schmitz*, 1933 (20); Zürich, Kunsthaus, *Französische Maler des XIX. Jahrhunderts*, 1933 (35).

LITERATURE: *Kunst und Künstler*, VIII, 1910, p. 22; Klossowski, 355 (identical with 379); *L'Amour de l'Art*, 1926, p. 340; Fuchs, 94; Cat. of the Oscar Schmitz Collection, privately printed (Wildenstein), 1937, No. 20.
Lent by Wildenstein & Company, New York

Probably about 1853 or earlier. A very small panel with the figure of the writer only, identical except for the face, is in a private collection in Paris (*Le dessinateur*; exhibited Durand-Ruel, 1878, No. 29). The drawing lent by Dr Bruck, Buenos Aires (see No. 122), is the only known study for the present picture.

39 Study of a Man's Head

Tête d'étude   PLATE 10C

Canvas: 26 by 34 (10¼ by 13⅜). L.r.: *h.D.*
PROVENANCE: Gwendoline E. Davies.
EXHIBITION: London, Burlington Fine Arts Club, *Pictures, Drawings and Sculpture of the French School of the last 100 Years*, 1922 (22).
LITERATURE: W. Sickert, in *Burl. Mag.*, June 1922, p. 266 and plate facing p. 266; Maison, in *Burl. Mag.*, April 1954, p. 105 and Fig. 9.
Lent by the National Museum of Wales, Cardiff

This study repeats the head of the central figure in the well-known painting *La Famille sur la Barricade*, in the Národni Museum, Prague of about 1848–49. That painting, however, was almost certainly left unfinished in many of the most important details. Daumier may have intended to take the subject up anew, and made a charcoal study of this head (see No. 132), followed some time later by the present study which is almost identical with the drawing.

40 Study of a Man's Head

Tête d'étude

Panel: 35 by 27 (13¾ by 10⅝).
PROVENANCE: Dupré; Hessel; private collection, Switzerland.
EXHIBITIONS: Durand-Ruel, 1878 (24); *Daumier-Gavarni*, 1923 (30).
LITERATURE: Alexandre, p. 374; Fuchs, 9; Scheiwiller, pl. X.
Lent by Marlborough Fine Art Ltd., London

Probably 1850–53. Jules Dupré, the Barbizon painter, was a friend of Daumier and owned a number of paintings and drawings by the artist.

41 Three Heads

Trois têtes—Trois personnages PLATE 22C

Grisaille on panel: 26·5 by 35 (10½ by 13¾).
PROVENANCE: Vollard; private collection, Paris; Wildenstein.
EXHIBITION: Beaux-Arts, 1901 (103).
Lent from a Private Collection, New York

42 Head of a Man

Tête d'homme—Tête d'insurgé

Panel: 28 by 21·5 (11 by 8½). L.r.: *h.D.*
PROVENANCE: Demelette.
EXHIBITION: Bibliothèque Nationale, 1958 (310).
LITERATURE: *Art Digest* (N.Y.), 15 May 1951, p. 16; Adhémar, pl. 40 ('*vers 1848*').
Lent by Wildenstein & Company, New York

43 The Bell-ringer

Tête de sonneur   PLATE 11B

Panel: 35 by 27 (13¾ by 10⅝). R.l.c.: *h.D.*
PROVENANCE: Boulard; Alexandre; Frau von D...; Margaret S. Davies.
EXHIBITIONS: Beaux-Arts, 1901 (4); Leicester Galleries, 1936 (85); Cardiff/Swansea, Arts Council exhibition, *Daumier, Millet, Courbet*, 1957 (5).
LITERATURE: *Cat. de la Vente Arsène Alexandre*, Paris, 1903, No. 23; *Kat. der Sammlung Frau von D...*, Munich, 1912, No. 15; Klossowski, 237 and pl. 128; Fuchs, 17b; Lassaigne, pl. 34; Adhémar, pl. 86 ('*vers 1856/63*'); Schweicher, pl. 5; Cat. of a Sale at Sotheby's, London, 4 May 1960, No. 106.
Lent from a Private Collection

Adhémar plausibly suggests that Daumier may have met the bell-ringer of Notre-Dame in the studio of his friend, Geoffroy-Dechaume the sculptor, which was situated in the immediate vicinity of the cathedral. The painting does not appear to be later than 1855.

44 Head of a Man

Tête d'homme—Tête d'étude

Panel: 21·5 by 16 (8½ by 6⅜). L.l.c.: *h.D.*
PROVENANCE: Camentron; A. Kann; Kelekian; W. P. Chrysler.

EXHIBITIONS: Beaux-Arts, 1901 (465); Chicago, Arts Club, *Origins of Modern Art*, 1941 (44); Richmond (Virginia), Museum of Fine Arts, *Works from the Walter P. Chrysler Collection*, an exhibition subsequently shown at the Philadelphia Museum of Art, 1941 (40).

LITERATURE: A. Alexandre, *La Collection Kelekian*, Paris, 1920, pl. 25; Klossowski, 449 and pl. 129; Cat. of the D. Kelekian Sale, New York, 1923, No. 95; Fuchs, 14a; *Art News* (N.Y.), 17 January 1941, p. 10; Cat. of the Chrysler Sale, London, 1959, No. 18.

Lent by Mr P. D. Christopoulos, London

Probably painted about 1860–65.

45 Two Men drinking

Les buveurs PLATE 22E

Panel: 37 by 28 (14⅝ by 11). L.l.c.: *h.D.*

PROVENANCE: Daubigny; H. Rouart; Knoedler; Adolph Lewisohn; Mrs Samuel A. Lewisohn; Mrs Margaret S. Lewisohn.

EXHIBITIONS: Paris, Galerie Martinet, *Exposition au profit des Amis de l'Enfance*, 1861 (141); Durand-Ruel, 1878 (49); Beaux-Arts, 1901 (68); New York, 1930 (69); Buffalo, Albright Art Gallery, *French Art of the 19th Century*, 1932 (15); Orangerie, 1934 (7); Chicago, Art Institute, *A Century of Progress*, 1934 (240); on loan to the Museum of Modern Art, New York, 1946.

LITERATURE: Alexandre, p. 375; *Cat. de la Vente H. Rouart*, Paris, 1912, I, No. 171; Klossowski, 264 and pl. 102; Fontainas, pl. 37; *Kunst und Künstler*, 1929, p. 419; Fuchs, 31; *The Fine Arts* (N.Y.), June 1933, p. 32; Lassaigne, pl. 47; Adhémar, pl. 85 ('*vers* 1856').

Lent by the Metropolitan Museum of Art, New York, Bequest of Margaret S. Lewisohn, 1954

46 The Serenade

La sérénade PLATE 12C

Panel: 30·2 by 39 (11⅞ by 15⅜).

PROVENANCE: Wisselingh; Sadler.

EXHIBITIONS: London, Royal Academy, *French Art, 1200–1900*, 1932 (383); London, Wildenstein Gallery, *The Kessler Collection*, 1948 (3); Cardiff/Swansea, Arts Council exhibition, *Daumier, Millet, Courbet*, 1957 (7).

LITERATURE: Sadleir, pl. 48, in colour; Fuchs, 116b; *Commemorative Cat. of the Exh. of French Art at the Royal Academy, 1932*, 1933, No. 328;

Scheiwiller, frontispiece in colour; Lassaigne, pl. 53; Adhémar, pl. 143 ('*vers* 1860').

Lent by Mrs A. Kessler, Rutland

The picture still bears the traditional title *La sérénade*, although its subject is clearly a *chanteuse de rue* singing in a garden restaurant. A considerably earlier drawing of a similar composition is in the City Art Museum, St. Louis (Mo.).

47 Couple singing

Le couple chantant PLATE 22J

Canvas: 36·5 by 28·5 (14⅜ by 11¼). L.l.c.: *h.D.*

PROVENANCE: Miethke (?); Hoogendijk.

LITERATURE: Fuchs, 281 and note on No. 33; Lassaigne, pl. 37; Cassou, pl. 7; Adhémar, pl. 106, in colour ('1856/60'); Schweicher, pl. 7; Ziller, pl. 89.

Lent by the Rijksmuseum, Amsterdam (on loan to the Stedelijk Museum)

Another version, only slightly more sketchy, belongs to a private collector in New York who has deposited it with the Fogg Art Museum, Cambridge (Mass.).

48 The amateur Trio

Trio d'amateurs

Panel: 22 by 25 (8⅝ by 9⅞). L.r.c.: *h. Daumier.*

PROVENANCE: Jacquette.

LITERATURE: Klossowski, 349; Fontainas, pl. 28; Escholier, 1923, p. 173, and 1930, pl. 31; Sadleir, pl. 47; Fuchs, 34a; Lassaigne, pl. 52; Adhémar, pl. 129 ('1863/66'); *Marseille, Revue municipale* (Marseilles), 29, 1956, p. 39.

Lent by the Musée du Petit Palais, Paris

49 Portrait of a Painter PLATE 11A

Portrait d'un peintre—Le peintre

Panel: 27·4 by 17·8 (10¾ by 7).

PROVENANCE: Geoffroy-Dechaume; Viau; Hansen (?); Reid & Lefevre.

EXHIBITIONS: Durand-Ruel, 1878 (40); Beaux-Arts, 1901 (86); Geneva, Musée d'Art et d'Histoire, *L'Ecoleançaise fr du XIXᵉ siècle*, 1918 (49).

LITERATURE: Alexandre, p. 374; *Cat. de la Vente Geoffroy-Dechaume*, Paris, 1893, No. 26; Klossowski, 389 and pl. 144; Fuchs, 2; Lassaigne, pl. 36; Adhémar, pl. 133 ('1863/66').

Lent by the National Gallery of Scotland, Edinburgh

A painted study for this picture, representing the

artist's head and shoulders only and without the palette, passed through the final Viau Sale in 1942. Its present whereabouts are not known.

50 The Painter before his Easel

Le peintre devant son tableau   PLATE 5

Panel: 33·5 by 26 (13⅛ by 10¼). L.l.c.: *h.D.*

PROVENANCE: Dollfus; P. Rosenberg; J. Strauss; Bignou; Reid & Lefevre; Burrell; Cargill.

EXHIBITIONS: Beaux-Arts, 1901 (65); Lefevre Galleries, 1927 (6).

LITERATURE: Geffroy, p. 18; Klossowski, 391 and pl. 145; Escholier, 1923, plate facing p. 121, 1930, pl. 46, and 1938, p. 173; Sadleir, pl. 61; Scheiwiller, pl. 1; Fuchs, 273; Fleischmann/Sachs, pl. 43; Lassaigne, pl. 55; Cassou, pl. 1; Adhémar, pl. 153 ('1863/66'); Schweicher, pl. 1.

Lent by the Phillips Collection, Washington

A study of a painter at work, but not a self-portrait. A very small version of this picture (11 by 8 cm.), perhaps a first study for it, is in the Barnes Foundation, Merion (Pa.), while an almost identical painting, on approximately the same scale, is in the Sterling and Francine Clark Art Institute, Williamstown (Mass.).

51 The Print Collectors

Les amateurs d'estampes

Panel: 27 by 36 (10⅝ by 14⅛).

PROVENANCE: Wisselingh.

LITERATURE: *The Studio* (special number), *Daumier and Gavarni*, 1904, plate facing p. D.XVIII; Klossowski, 375F; *Kunst und Künstler*, 1923, p. 122; Fuchs, 100b.

Lent by the Städtische Kunsthalle, Mannheim

Painted about 1855–60.

52 The Connoisseurs

Les amateurs de tableaux

Panel: 33 by 23·5 (13 by 9¼).

PROVENANCE: Vollard; Dubourg; Matthiesen; Oppenheimer.

EXHIBITIONS: Beaux-Arts, 1901 (97?); Bibliothèque Nationale, 1958 (219).

LITERATURE: Maison, in *Gazette des Beaux-Arts*, May/June 1958, p. 243 and Fig. 3.

Lent by Paul Rosenberg & Company, New York

Probably about 1855–60, this is the first painted sketch for the picture in the collection of Mrs Harris Jonas, New York. The final version, as well as the very small *croquis* in the Jacques Dupont Collection, Paris, shows the three figures full-length.

53 The Connoisseurs   PLATE 13C

Les amateurs—Amateurs de peinture

Canvas: 23·5 by 31 (9¼ by 12¼). L.l.c.: *h. Daumier*.

PROVENANCE: Bureau; Matthiesen; Goldschmidt; van Beuningen.

EXHIBITIONS: Durand-Ruel, 1878 (12); *La Caricature*, 1888 (364); Paris, *Exposition Centennale*, 1900 (184); Beaux-Arts, 1901 (14); Orangerie, 1934 (20); on loan to the Museum Boymans, Rotterdam, 1939 and 1949; Paris, Petit Palais, *Chefs d'œuvre de la Collection D. G. van Beuningen*, 1952 (171).

LITERATURE: Alexandre, p. 374; Klossowski, 369; *Cat. de la Vente P. Bureau*, Paris, 1927, No. 96; Fuchs, 98; Escholier, 1930, pl. 32; Fleischmann/Sachs, pl. 56; D. Hannema, Cat. of the van Beuningen Collection, Rotterdam, 1949, No. 129 and pl. 168, in colour.

Lent by the Museum Boymans-van Beuningen, Rotterdam

Probably painted about 1860. A related version, with the *amateurs* shown seated, is in the Sterling and Francine Clark Art Institute, Williamstown (Mass.).

54 The Print Collector

L'amateur d'estampes

Panel: 35·6 by 25·4 (14 by 10). L.l. (on the portfolio): *h.D.*

PROVENANCE: Barbizon House.

EXHIBITIONS: London, Tate Gallery, *Loan Exhibition of the Burrell Collection*, 1924 (29); Arts Council travelling exhibition, *French Paintings of the 19th Century from the Burrell Collection*, 1950 (21).

LITERATURE: *Barbizon House: An Illustrated Souvenir for 1923*, pl. 16; Sadleir, pl. 26, in colour; J. Laver, *19th Century French Painting*, 1927, frontispiece, in colour; D. Talbot Rice, in *Scottish Art Review* (Glasgow), 3, 1946, p. 5.

Lent by the Corporation of Glasgow, Burrell Collection

A very similar version, somewhat lighter in colour, is now in the Art Institute of Chicago. The histories of these two paintings have been repeatedly confused in the Daumier literature.

55 Two Print Collectors

Amateurs d'estampes—Deux artistes debout regardant un dessin   PLATE 13A

Panel: 35 by 26 (13¾ by 10¼).

PROVENANCE: Durand-Ruel; Dr A. Hahnloser.

EXHIBITIONS: Beaux-Arts, 1901 (35); Paris, Gazette des Beaux-Arts, *La Peinture française du XIXe siècle en Suisse*, 1935 (39); Paris, Orangerie, *Monticelli et le Baroque Provençal*, 1953 (31).

LITERATURE: Klossowski, 386 and pl. 146; Fuchs, 108; Lassaigne, pl. 73, in colour; Lassaigne, 1946, p. 21, in colour; Schweicher, 1954, pl. 20.

Lent by Professor Dr Hans R. Hahnloser, Berne

Probably painted about 1865–68. Two further versions of this composition are known, both on canvas: the little picture in the collection of Monsieur Maurice Gobin, Paris (23 by 18 cm.) is presumably a first sketch, while the version in the Ghent Museum (39 by 31 cm.) is practically identical with the present picture.

56 The Print Collector

L'amateur d'estampes   PLATE 13B

Panel: 35 by 26 (13¾ by 10¼). L.l.c.: *h.D.*

PROVENANCE: Lutz; Esnault-Pelterie.

EXHIBITIONS: Paris, Galerie Georges Petit, *Chefs d'œuvre de l'Art français*, 1910 (39); Orangerie, 1934 (22); Philadelphia, 1937 (2).

LITERATURE: Geffroy, plate facing p. 4; *Les Arts*, May 1902, p. 30, and June 1906, p. 14; *Cat. de la Vente Ggs. Lutz*, Paris, 1902, No. 46; Klossowski, 374 and pl. 139; Fontainas, pl. 3; Escholier, 1923, plate facing p. 52, 1930, pl. 8, and 1938, frontispiece in colour; Fuchs, 106; S. Rocheblave, *French Painting of the Nineteenth Century*, 1936, pl. 49; C. Roger-Marx, *Daumier*, Paris, 1938, p. 37.

Lent by the Commissioners of Fairmount Park, by courtesy of the Philadelphia Museum of Art, W. P. Wilstach Collection

In addition to two black chalk sketches, there is a small painted study for this well-known composition (New Orleans, private collection). A closely related version is in the Musée du Petit Palais, Paris.

57 On the Stage

Scène de théâtre

Canvas: 28 by 22 (11 by 5⅝).

PROVENANCE: Vollard; Schuler.

EXHIBITION: Beaux-Arts, 1901 (90).

LITERATURE: Klossowski, 91; Fuchs, 119.

Lent by the Kunsthaus, Zürich

Painted about 1850. The actors are sometimes identified as characters in a Molière play.

58 At the Theatre

Au théâtre

Panel: 33 by 41 (13 by 16⅛). L.r.c.: *h.D.*

PROVENANCE: Vollard (?); Viau; Druet; Schuler.

EXHIBITION: Vienna, *Sezession*, 1904 (38).

LITERATURE: *Cat. de la 2e Vente Dr Viau*, Paris, 1907, No. 23; Klossowski, 90; Fuchs, 135b.

Lent by the Kunsthaus, Zürich

Painted about 1855–60.

59 At the Theatre

Au théâtre—Au théâtre: Les six spectateurs   PLATE 22K

Canvas: 34 by 40 (13⅜ by 15¾). L.l.c.: *h.D.*

PROVENANCE: L. Tual (?); Dr Paulin; G. Bernheim; Wildenstein.

LITERATURE: *Cat. of a Sale at the Salle Drouot*, Paris, 21 November 1901 (Dr Paulin?), No. 15; Klossowski, 87; Lassaigne, pl. 135; Adhémar, pl. 139 ('vers 1862'); Schweicher, pl. 49.

Lent by the Nathan Cummings Family, Chicago

60 Doctor Diafoirus

Le médecin Diafoirus—Une tête de médecin de Molière   PLATE 12A

Panel: 23 by 17.5 (9 by 6⅞). R.l.c.: *h. Daumier.*

PROVENANCE: Aubry; Hazard; François; M. Bernheim.

EXHIBITIONS: Durand-Ruel, 1878 (6); Beaux-Arts, 1901 (470).

LITERATURE: Alexandre, p. 373; *Cat. de la Vente P. A*[ubry]., Paris, 1897, No. 4; *Cat. de la Vente Hazard*, Paris, 1919, No. 99; *Cat. de la Vente*

François, Paris, 1935, No. 1; Klossowski, 65; Fuchs, 17a.

Lent by Dr and Mrs Harry Bakwin, New York

Painted about 1865–68. Doctor Diafoirus is a character from Molière's *Malade Imaginaire*, symbolizing the ignorant and pretentious physician.

61 Leaving the Theatre PLATE 15B
Sortie de théâtre—Au théâtre—L'attente
Panel: 33·3 by 41·2 (13⅛ by 16¼). L.l.c.: *h.D.*
PROVENANCE: Vollard; H. Nathan; Wildenstein.
EXHIBITIONS: Beaux-Arts, 1901 (95); Matthiesen, 1926 (17).
LITERATURE: Geffroy, p. 14; *Kunst und Künstler*, XV, 1917, p. 106; Klossowski, 103C; Escholier, 1923, plate facing p. 100, and 1930, pl. 37; Fuchs, 40; Lassaigne, pl. 130.
Lent by Mr and Mrs Charles W. Engelhard, Far Hills, N.J.

62 Le Malade Imaginaire PLATE 12B
Panel: 27 by 35 (10⅝ by 13¾). L.r.c.: *h. Daumier.*
PROVENANCE: Schagé; Esnault-Pelterie.
EXHIBITIONS: Durand-Ruel, 1878 (31); Paris, *Exposition Centennale*, 1900 (188); Paris, Galerie Georges Petit, *Chefs d'œuvre de l'Ecole française*, 1910 (46); Orangerie, 1934 (30); Philadelphia, 1937 (13).
LITERATURE: Geffroy, plate facing p. 18; Klossowski, 66 and pl. 85; Fontainas, pl. 22; Escholier, 1923, plate facing p. 90, 1930, pl. 12, and 1938, p. 141; Fuchs, 128; Fleischmann/Sachs, pl. 41; Kalitina, pl. 73.
Lent by the Philadelphia Museum of Art

Painted about 1860–62. A more sketchy version of this composition, with two figures only, is in the Barnes Foundation, Merion (Pa.).

63 Scene from a Molière Play PLATE 15A
Scène de Molière—Scène de théâtre—Un Scapin—un Scapin et un Géronte
Panel: 31·3 by 23·2 (12⅜ by 9⅛).
PROVENANCE: Turquois; Dulac.
EXHIBITIONS: Durand-Ruel, 1878 (84); *La Caricature*, 1888 (375 ?); Beaux-Arts, 1901 (78).
LITERATURE: Alexandre, p. 374; Klossowski, 74; P. Vitry, in *Beaux-Arts*, 1928, p. 87; Escholier,

1930, pl. 27; Fleischmann/Sachs, pl. 40; Lassaigne, pl. 137, in colour; Lassaigne, 1946, p. 35, in colour; Adhémar, pl. 126, in colour ('*vers* 1860'); Schweicher, pl. 55; Ziller, pl. 98.
Lent by the Musée du Louvre, Paris

A somewhat different composition—though close in spirit—depicting the same scene from either *L'Avare* or the *Fourberies de Scapin* is in the Fogg Art Museum, Cambridge (Mass.) (exhibited Durand-Ruel, 1878 (83)). The two paintings have very similar dimensions and the same early history. Two slight black chalk drawings, *Deux Personnages de Comédie*, in the collections of Monsieur R. Lebel and Monsieur C. Roger-Marx, Paris, are studies for the present picture.

64 The Troubadour
Page jouant de la mandoline—Le Page—
Le guitariste PLATE 14C
Canvas: 78 by 56·2 (30¾ by 22⅛). L.r.: *h.D.*
PROVENANCE: Doria; Vollard; Cassirer; Fuchs; Wildenstein; Hanna.
EXHIBITIONS: Beaux-Arts, 1901 (101); Matthiesen, 1926 (41); New York, 1930 (57).
LITERATURE: *Cat. de la Vente Comte A. Doria*, Paris, 1899, No. 132; Klossowski, 75 and pl. 52; Fuchs, 117; *Cahiers d'Art*, III, 1928, p. 196; Maison, in *Burl. Mag.*, June 1956, p. 200 and Fig. 17.
Lent by the Cleveland Museum of Art, Bequest of Leonard C. Hanna, Jr.

Probably painted in the mid-1860s. A charcoal study closely connected with this painting, is in the British Museum (see No. 146).

65 The Wrestlers
Les Lutteurs PLATE 14D
Panel: 42 by 27 (16½ by 10⅝). L.l.c.: *h. Daumier.*
PROVENANCE: Daubigny; Sarlin; Heilbuth; Reid & Lefevre; Hansen.
EXHIBITIONS: Durand-Ruel, 1878 (55); Beaux-Arts, 1901 (71); Paris, Galerie Georges Petit, *Chefs d'œuvre de l'Ecole française*, 1910 (42); Geneva, Musée d'Art et d'Histoire, *L'école française du XIXe siècle*, 1918 (47).
LITERATURE: Geoffroy, plate facing p. 10; *Cat. de la Vente L. Sarlin*, Paris, 1918, No. 26; Klossowski, 178 and pl. 82; Fontainas, pl. 38; Escholier, 1923, p. 194; Fuchs, 115; *Cahiers d'Art*, III, 1928, p. 189;

Cassou, pl. 40; Adhémar, pl. 155, in colour ('*vers 1865/8*'); Maison, in *Burl. Mag.*, June 1956, p. 200 and Figs. 21–23.

Lent by the Ordrupgaard Collection, Copenhagen

Apart from the pencil sketch for the whole composition (see No. 176), several other studies for the detail of the wrestlers in the arena are known.

66 Head of a Buffoon

Tête de pasquin   PLATE 14B

Panel: 22 by 16·5 (8⅝ by 6½). R.u.c.: *h. Daumier*.

PROVENANCE: Doria; Dorigny; Durand-Ruel; Bensinger; Barkhausen; Oppenheimer.

EXHIBITION: Durand-Ruel, 1878 (35).

LITERATURE: Alexandre, p. 373; *Cat. de la Vente Comte A. Doria*, Paris, 1899, No. 131; Klossowski, 74A; Escholier, 1923, p. 155; Fuchs, 127a; Lassaigne, pl. 144; Schweicher, pl. 57.

Lent by Mr Emery Reves

Painted about 1855–58.

67 Head of a Clown

Tête de paillasse—Pierrot   PLATE 14A

Panel: 22 by 16·5 (8⅝ by 6½). L.r.c.: *h. Daumier*.

PROVENANCE: de Bellio; Donop de Monhy; P. Rosenberg; S. Brown; Wildenstein.

EXHIBITIONS: Beaux-Arts, 1901 (33); Basle, Société des Beaux-Arts, *Peinture française*, 1921 (49); Matthiesen, 1926 (63).

LITERATURE: Klossowski, 207; Fuchs, 118a; Lassaigne, pl. 145, in colour; Lassaigne, 1946, p. 25, in colour; Adhémar, pl. 161, in colour ('1862/65'); Schweicher, pl. 58.

Lent by Lady Berlin, Oxfordshire

Although certainly painted much later, this study may well have been intended to serve as a companion picture to the *Head of a Buffoon* (see No. 66).

68 A Waiting Room

Une salle d'attente   PLATE 23E

Oil on paper, laid down on panel: 31 by 24·7 (12¼ by 9¾).

PROVENANCE: Bureau; P. Rosenberg; Goodyear.

EXHIBITIONS: Beaux-Arts, 1901 (19); New York, 1930 (75); Orangerie, 1934 (5).

LITERATURE: Klossowski, 247; *Cat. de la Vente P. Bureau*, Paris, 1927, No. 97; *L'Amour de l'Art*, 1927, p. 149; Fuchs, 46; Escholier, 1930, pl. 35, and 1938, p. 35; Fleischmann/Sachs, pl. 71; Lassaigne, pl. 126.

Lent by the Albright Art Gallery, Buffalo

In spite of some differences in the composition, the pen and wash drawing in the T. E. Hanley Collection, Bradford (Pa.), is very closely connected with this partly unfinished picture. Furthermore, a woodcut published in *Monde illustré* in March 1862 is very close to it.

69 A Third-class Railway Carriage

Un wagon de troisième classe   PLATE 16B

Canvas: 67 by 93 (26⅜ by 36⅝). L.r.c. (on a box): *h. Daumier*.

PROVENANCE: Brame; Pillet; Doria; Petit; Gallimard; Cassirer; Murray; Wisselingh; C. G. Edwards.

EXHIBITIONS: Durand-Ruel, 1878 (62); *La Caricature*, 1888 (354); Paris, *Exposition Centennale*, 1889 (232); Beaux-Arts, 1901 (43); Zürich, Künstlergesellschaft, *Exposition d'Art français*, 1917 (558 bis); on loan to the Tate Gallery, 1924 and 1926; Lefevre Galleries, 1927 (1); New York, 1930 (67); Ottawa, National Gallery of Canada, *French Painting*, 1934 (40); Montreal, Art Association, *Masterpieces of Painting*, 1942 (55); Toledo Museum of Art, Ohio, *The Spirit of Modern France*, subsequently shown at the Toronto Art Gallery, 1946 (29).

LITERATURE: Alexandre, p. 375; *Cat. de la Vente Brame*, Paris, 1882, No. 7; *Cat. de la Vente Comte A. Doria*, Paris, 1899, No. 127; Geffroy, p. 12; *Les Arts*, September, 1908, p. 7; Klossowski, 252; Fontainas, pl. 12; Escholier, 1923, p. 145, and 1930, pl. 11; Cat. of the Sir James Murray Sale, London, 1927, No. 37; *Cahiers d'Art*, III, 1928, p. 195; Fuchs, 43; Lassaigne, pl. 123; A. Mongan, in *Gazette des Beaux-Arts*, 1937, p. 253; *Burlington Magazine*, 1938, plate facing p. 280 (wrongly located as in the Metropolitan Museum); A. Rosen and H. Marceau, in *Journal of the Walters Art Gallery* (Baltimore), III, 1940, Fig. 13; *Art Digest* (N.Y.), October 1946, p. 6; *Art Quarterly* (Detroit), X, 1947, p. 226; Adhémar, note on pl. 147 ('*vers 1862*').

Lent by the National Gallery of Canada, Ottawa

The only completely finished painted version of this famous composition; it was probably preceded by the very similar—though not identical—water-colour in the Walters Art Gallery, Baltimore (see No. 190). A very elaborate tracing of the painting, without the carriage roof (52 by 86 cm.), was lent by Vollard to the 1901 exhibition at the Ecole des Beaux-Arts. It was presumably this tracing which was used for the transfer of the composition to a new canvas, i.e. the unfinished painting in the Metropolitan Museum, New York. A further tracing (68 by 92 cm., now in the Cluzot Collection, Paris) must have been taken from the back of that tracing, as it shows the picture in reverse.

70 A Third-class Carriage

Un wagon de troisième classe   PLATE 16A

Panel: 26 by 34 (10¼ by 13⅜). L.r.: *h. Daumier*.

PROVENANCE: Pelpel; Bernheim Jeune; Knoedler; Hill.

EXHIBITIONS: Durand-Ruel, 1878 (70); *La Caricature*, 1888 (372); Minneapolis, Institute of Arts, *The Collection of James J. Hill*, 1958 (p. 3 of the catalogue); on loan to the Metropolitan Museum, New York, 1958.

LITERATURE: Alexandre, p. 375; *Cat. de la Vente M. P[elpel].*, Paris, 21 December 1908, No. 9; Klossowski, 275B and pl. 100; Fontainas, pl. 11; Escholier, 1923, p. 87, and 1930, pl. 30; Fuchs, 45b; Fleischmann/Sachs, pl. 72; Lassaigne, pl. 125; Cassou, pl. 32; Schweicher, pl. 47.

Lent by Mr Anson Beard, New York

The only one among Daumier's *Wagons de troisième classe* for which no study appears to be preserved. Probably the earliest among related compositions.

71 Washerwomen on the Steps of the Quay

PLATE 23A

Les laveuses du Quai d'Anjou—Les blanchisseuses—Les laveuses sur l'escalier

Panel: 47 by 32·5 (18½ by 12¾). L.r.c.: *h. Daumier*.

PROVENANCE: Alexandre; Graat; Silberberg; Matthiesen; Goeritz.

EXHIBITIONS: Matthiesen, 1926 (30); Leicester Galleries, 1936 (90).

LITERATURE: *Cat. de la Vente Arsène Alexandre*, Paris, 1903, No. 16; Klossowski, 221 and pl. 93; Fuchs, 74; Lassaigne, pl. 94; Adhémar, pl. 113 ('*vers* 1860/62') (The history given for this picture refers to the other version, see below); Schweicher, pl. 34.

Lent by Mrs I. G. Selver, New York

This study was painted prior to a more finished version in the Gerstenberg Collection (litho-graphed by Lunois in 1862).

72 The Washerwoman

La laveuse—Une laveuse au Quai d'Anjou   PLATE 23D

Panel: 28·5 by 19·7 (11¼ by 7¾). L.l.c.: *h.D.*

PROVENANCE: Lutz; Morot; Ed. Davis; Reid & Lefevre; Knoedler; Goodyear.

EXHIBITIONS: Probably Paris, Salon, 1861 (800); Lefevre Galleries, 1927 (10).

LITERATURE: *Cat. de la Vente Ggs. Lutz*, Paris, 1902, No. 49; *Studio*, Vol. 54, 1915, p. 83; Klossowski, 225; Adhémar, note on pl. 114 ('*vers* 1860').

Lent by the Albright Art Gallery, Buffalo

The smallest and probably the first of several versions of this well-known composition. The version in the Metropolitan Museum of Art, New York, is dated 1863.

73 The heavy Burden

Le fardeau—La blanchisseuse   PLATE 23G

Panel: 19·5 by 12·5 (7⅝ by 4⅞). L.l.c.: *h.D.*

PROVENANCE: Dr A. Hahnloser.

EXHIBITIONS: Winterthur, Kunstmuseum, *Meisterwerke aus Privatsammlungen*, 1922 (29); Cannes, Musée, *La Provence et ses peintres au XIXe siècle*, 1929 (12); Lucerne, Kunstmuseum, *Meisterwerke der Sammlung Hahnloser*, 1940 (36).

Lent by Frau Lisa Jäggli-Hahnloser, Winterthur

Of the six known versions of this subject, three, which differ from each other more obviously than from the remaining three, are shown here (see Nos. 74 and 75). With the exception of the present picture, which is so far unrecorded in the Daumier literature, the histories of the respective paintings have almost invariably been confused. The two compositions which are closest to this little study, except in size, are in the Gerstenberg Collection and in the Národní Galerie, Prague. Adhémar dates the whole group around 1860.

74 The heavy Burden

Le Fardeau—La blanchisseuse   PLATE 17

Canvas: 147 by 95 (57⅞ by 37½). L.r.c.: *h.D.*

PROVENANCE: Mme Daumier; Alexandre; Hertz; Boulanger.

EXHIBITION: Paris, Galerie Charpentier, *Cent Chefs d'œuvre de l'Art français 1750–1950*, 1950 (19).
LITERATURE: Fuchs, 292a; Lassaigne, pl. 96; Adhémar, pl. 115; Schweicher, pl. 36.
Lent by Monsieur Ernest Gutzwiller, Paris.

See note on No. 73.

75 The heavy Burden

Le Fardeau—La laveuse

Peinture à l'essence (?) on panel: 40 by 30 (15¾ by 11¾). L.l.c.: *h. Daumier.*

EXHIBITIONS: Glasgow, International Exhibition, 1901 (1411); on loan to the Tate Gallery, 1924.
LITERATURE: Fuchs, 293b.
Lent by the Corporation of Glasgow, Burrell Collection

The treatment of the background in this picture, as well as the face of the woman, differ from the preceding versions. A virtually identical composition (44·5 by 36·8 cm.) is in the Robin Howard Collection, London. See note on No. 73.

76 Street Scene

Une scène de rue—La sortie de l'écolier— Le Fardeau

Panel: 27 by 21·3 (10⅝ by 8⅜).

PROVENANCE: Desfossés; Camentron; Gallimard; Cassirer (?); Blumenfeld; Matthiesen; Goud-stikker; van Beuningen.
EXHIBITIONS: Durand-Ruel, 1878 (61, as *Départ pour l'école*); Matthiesen, 1926 (69); on loan to the Museum Boymans, Rotterdam, 1949; Paris, Petit Palais, *Chefs d'œuvre de la Collection D. G. van Beuningen*, 1952 (169).
LITERATURE: *Cat. de la Vente Victor Desfossés*, Paris, 1899 (26); Klossowski, 228B; Fuchs, 71; D. Hannema, Cat. of the van Beuningen Collection, Rotterdam, 1949, No. 127 and pl. 171.
Lent by the Museum Boymans-van Beuningen, Rotterdam

A composition clearly evolved from the theme of *Le Fardeau*. A picture of the same dimensions, *Femme et enfant sur un pont*, in the Phillips Collection, Washington, shows the two central figures only, with a background similar to that of *Le Fardeau*.

77 Workmen in a Street

Ouvriers dans une rue—Dans la rue

Panel: 11·5 by 16 (4½ by 6½).

PROVENANCE: H. Rouart; Bernheim Jeune (?); Gwendoline E. Davies.
LITERATURE: Alexandre, p. 375; *Cat. de la Vente H. Rouart*, Paris, 1912, I, No. 172; Klossowski, 290 and pl. 13; Fuchs, 76a; Lassaigne, pl. 46; Cassou, pl. 24; Maison, listed in *Burl. Mag.*, April 1954, p. 105, No. 2.
Lent by the National Museum of Wales, Cardiff

Probably painted not later than about 1840.

78 The Moonlight Walk

Les noctambules—Dans une rue de Paris —Effet de claire de lune

Panel: 28 by 18·7 (11 by 7⅜).

PROVENANCE: Saucède; H. Rouart; Gwendoline E. Davies.
EXHIBITION: *La Caricature*, 1888 (359).
LITERATURE: *Cat. de la Vente A. Saucède*, Paris, 1879, No. 11; Alexandre, p. 375 (?); *Cat. de la Vente H. Rouart*, Paris, 1912, I, No. 168; Klossow-ski, 291 and pl. 15; Fuchs, 49; Lassaigne, pl. 127; Maison, in *Apollo*, July/August 1952, Fig. I; Maison, listed in *Burl. Mag.*, April 1954, p. 105, No. 1; Adhémar, pl. 26, in colour ('1843/48'); Schweicher, pl. 45; Ziller, pl. 102.
Lent by the National Museum of Wales, Cardiff

79 Children running

Enfants courant—Sortie de l'école

Panel: 26·5 by 21 (10½ by 8¼). L.l.c.: *h.D.*

PROVENANCE: Bignou; Wisselingh; ten Cate.
EXHIBITION: Zürich, Kunsthaus, 1933 (45); Rotterdam, Museum Boymans, *Kersttentoonstelling*, 1934-35 (26), and *Kunstschatten uit Nederlandse Versamelingen*, 1955 (181).
LITERATURE: Fuchs, 70; D. Hannema, Cat. of the H.E. ten Cate Collection, Rotterdam, 1955, I, No. 45; Cat. of the ten Cate Sale, London, 1958, No. 69.
Lent by Monsieur Leonard C. Stein, Geneva

Painted about 1852–54.

80 Man on a Rope

L'homme à la corde—Le badigeonneur— L'évasion

Canvas: 113 by 73·5 (44½ by 28⅞).

PROVENANCE: Hazard; Barbazanges; Wisselingh; H. S. Southam.

EXHIBITION: Basle, Société des Beaux-Arts, *Peinture Française*, 1921 (54 or 55).

LITERATURE: *Cat. de la Vente Hazard*, Paris, 1919, No. 104 or 105; Klossowski, 230 or 231 (giving wrong measurements); Fuchs, 290.

Lent by the National Gallery of Canada, Ottawa

Of the three known versions of this composition this is probably the earliest. The artist may not have been satisfied with it, scraped off large areas of paint and finally left it unfinished (see No. 81).

81 Man on a Rope

L'homme à la corde—Le badigeonneur—L'évasion

Canvas: 113 by 73·5 (44½ by 28⅞).

PROVENANCE: Hazard; Barbazanges; Bignou; Reid & Lefevre; Scott & Fowles; J. Kerrigan; E. S. Kerrigan; Schnittjer.

EXHIBITIONS: Basle, Société des Beaux-Arts, *Peinture française*, 1921 (54 or 55); Cambridge (Mass.), Fogg Art Museum, *French Painting of the 19th and 20th Centuries*, 1929 (19); New York, 1930 (60).

LITERATURE: *Cat. de la Vente Hazard*, Paris, 1919, No. 104 or 105; Klossowski, 230 or 231 (giving wrong measurements); Fontainas, pl. 41; Fuchs, 89b; Lassaigne, pl. 99; Cat. of the E. Salter-Kerrigan Sale, New York, 1942, No. 282; Cat. of the F. Schnittjer Sale, New York, 1943, No. 22; Adhémar, pl. 119, in colour ('*vers* 1860').

Lent by the Museum of Fine Arts, Boston

The second version of this composition (see No. 80). The final version, in the collection of Mme David-Weill, Paris, is on panel, reduced in size to 28 by 18 cm.

82 The Butcher

Le boucher, Marché Montmartre—Le boucher à son étal—Le boucher de Montmartre   PLATE 23C

Panel: 22·5 by 28 (8⅞ by 11). L.l.c.: *h. Daumier*.

PROVENANCE: Geoffroy-Dechaume; Hazard; Bielle; Daber.

EXHIBITIONS: Durand-Ruel, 1878 (41); Beaux-Arts, 1901 (471).

LITERATURE: Alexandre, p. 375; *Cat. de la Vente Geoffroy-Dechaume*, 1893, No. 25; Klossowski, 244; Fuchs, p. 4, listed as missing.

Lent by M. Knoedler & Company, New York.

This is possibly the only painting of a satirical subject in Daumier's *œuvre*. The brush work is almost identical with that of a lithograph (Delteil 3015) which appeared in Paris as one of a series in *Charivari* in November 1857; these cartoons made fun of a 'revolt' among the butchers over some curtailment of their privileges. The caption under the lithograph reads '*Vot*' *bourgeois est-y pour la liberté de la boucherie?*'

83 Three Lawyers in Conversation

Trois avocats—Trois avocats causant
          PLATE 18B

Panel: 40·6 by 33 (16 by 13). L.l.c.: *h. Daumier*.

PROVENANCE: H. Rouart; Blumenthal.

EXHIBITIONS: *La Caricature*, 1888 (357?); Paris, *Exposition Centennale*, 1889 (233); New York, 1930 (63); Orangerie, 1934 (40); on loan to the Boston Museum of Fine Arts, 1935; San Francisco, *Golden Gate Exhibition*, 1940 (257).

LITERATURE: *Cat. de la Vente H. Rouart*, I, Paris, 1912, No. 162; Klossowski, 122 and pl. 70; Escholier, 1923, pl. 186, 1930, pl. 42, and 1938, p. 91; *International Studio* (N.Y.), Sept. 1929, p. 22; Fuchs, 23; Fleischmann/Sachs, pl. 19; Lassaigne, pl. 74; Adhémar, pl. 23 ('1843–46'); Ziller, pl. 103, in colour.

Lent by the Phillips Collection, Washington

There is an important (though unpublished) water-colour in the Sterling and Francine Clark Art Institute, Williamstown (Mass.), in which Daumier repeats all the essential details of this composition, apart from the left portion of the background. Adhémar's suggested date for the painting appears to be somewhat too early; the (much later) water-colour, in any case, is typical in style of the *grandes aquarelles* of 1860–63.

84 Members of the Bar

Les avocats   PLATE 18C

Panel: 22·2 by 28 (8¾ by 11). L.l.c.: *h.D.*

PROVENANCE: Boussod & Valadon; Wisselingh (1896); A. A. Pope family; Mrs J. W. Riddle; Durand-Ruel; S. Salz.

EXHIBITION: Detroit, Art Institute, *From David to Courbet*, 1950 (92).

LITERATURE: La Farge and Jaccaci, *Bibliography for the noteworthy Paintings in American Private Collections: The Bibliography of the Collection of Mr Alfred Atmore Pope*, New York, n.d. (*c.* 1910), p. 4 and plate facing p. 4; Klossowski, 1.

Lent by Mr and Mrs Charles Goldman, New York

A very small black chalk sketch for the centre part of this picture is in the collection of Monsieur R. Leybold, Paris.

85 A Lawyer and his Client
L'avocat et son client

Panel: 14 by 13 (5½ by 5⅛). L.l.c.: *h. Daumier.*

PROVENANCE: Coleman; Bernheim Jeune.

LITERATURE: *Cat. de la Vente Mme Coleman*, Paris, 1917, No. 16; Klossowski, 113C; Fuchs, 277a; Escholier, 1938, p. 48; Lassaigne, pl. 83b; Schweicher, pl. 29.

Lent by Monsieur Jacques Dubourg, Paris

Painted about 1854–56. Several imitations of this little study are known to exist; the crudest of them enlarges the composition to 63 by 50·5 cm.

86 A Lawyer reading a Document
L'avocat lisant—Dans la salle des pas-perdus—La lecture du placet   PLATE 18A

Canvas: 41·5 by 33 (16⅜ by 13).

PROVENANCE: Corot; Alexandre (?); Tavernier; Gallimard; Druet; Ed. Bühler.

EXHIBITIONS: Beaux-Arts, 1901 (75); St Petersburg, Institut Français, *Centennale de l'Art français*, 1912 (240); Basle, Société des Beaux-Arts, *Peinture française*, 1921 (46); Paris, Gazette des Beaux-Arts, *La Peinture française du XIXᵉ siècle en Suisse*, 1938 (38a); Winterthur, Kunstmuseum, *Der unbekannte Winterthurer Privatbesitz*, 1942 (77); Paris, Orangerie, *Monticelli et le Baroque Provençal*, 1953 (29); Paris, Petit Palais, *De Géricault à Matisse, Chefs d'œuvre français des Collections suisses*, 1959 (36); Wolfsburg, Stadthalle, *Französische Malerei: von Delacroix bis Picasso*, 1961 (39).

LITERATURE: *Cat. de la Vente A. Tavernier*, Paris, 1900, No. 14, and 1907, No. 9; Klossowski, 116; Fuchs, 22a; Lassaigne, pl. 81, in colour; Lassaigne, 1946, p. 27, in colour; Adhémar, pl. 21, in colour ('1843/46'); Schweicher, pl. 24.

Lent by Dr Robert Bühler, Winterthur

A *reprise* of the same composition, in water-colour and finished in all essential details, is in the Esnault-Pelterie Collection.

87 Don Quixote in the Mountains
Don Quichotte dans les montagnes
PLATE 20A

Panel: 39 by 32 (15⅜ by 12⅝). L.l.c.: *h. Daumier.*

PROVENANCE: Aubry; Behrens; Goerg; Bignou; Reid & Lefevre; Robert T. Paine.

EXHIBITIONS: Durand-Ruel, 1878 (4); Beaux-Arts, 1901 (45); St Petersburg, Institut Français, *Centennale de l'Art français*, 1912 (245); Cambridge (Mass.), Fogg Art Museum, *French Art*, 1929 (18); Orangerie, 1934 (39).

LITERATURE: Alexandre, p. 373; *Cat. de la Vente P. A[ubry]., Paris, 1897, No. 3; *Cat. d'une Vente anon.*, Paris, 24 March 1900, No. 5; Geffroy, p. 6; *Cat. de la Vente Goerg*, Paris, 1910, No. 24; Klossowski, 41 and pl. 44; Fontainas, pl. 34; Sadleir, pl. 13; *Cahiers d'Art*, III, 1928, p. 197; Fuchs, 163; *The Arts* (N.Y.), 1929, I, pl. 63; Escholier, 1930, pl. 29, and 1938, p. 125; Fleischmann/Sachs, pl. 7; Lassaigne, pl. 157; Cassou, pl. 50; Kalitina, pl. 75; Schweicher, pl. 63; *Marseille, Revue municipale* (Marseilles), III, No. 29, p. 34.

Lent by Mr Richard C. Paine, Boston (Mass.)

Probably one of the earlier Don Quixote compositions (about 1850?). The study of Don Quixote on a white horse in the Munich Staatsgalerie appears to be considerably later in style; it might well be a *reprise* of the central part of the present picture and not, as is generally assumed, a study for it.

88 Sancho Panza seated under a Tree
Sancho Pansa assis sous un arbre
PLATE 19

Canvas: 100 by 82 (39⅜ by 32¼). L.r.c.: *h.D.*

PROVENANCE: Vienna art market (1908).

LITERATURE: *Cicerone* (Leipzig), 1912, p. 588; *Kunst und Künstler*, 1912, p. 539; Klossowski, 46A; Fuchs, plate facing p. 40; Fleischmann/Sachs, plate facing p. 10, in colour.

Lent by the Kunsthistorisches Museum, Vienna

Probably painted in the mid-1850s. The panel painting of the same composition in the Oskar Reinhart Collection, Winterthur (Adhémar: '*vers* 1868'), is more probably a later *reprise* for the present picture than a study for it.

89 Don Quixote and Sancho Panza

PLATE 21A

Canvas: 66 by 116 (26 by 45⅝), with an additional
strip of unpainted canvas folded back at the top.

PROVENANCE: Célos; Cassirer; Remarque; Feilchenfeldt.

EXHIBITIONS: On loan first to the Metropolitan
Museum, New York, and subsequently to the
Kunsthaus, Zürich, 1958–60.

Lent from a Private Collection, Zürich

An unfinished painting, with the squaring from
transfer clearly visible. A tracing of one of several
versions of an identically composed drawing, which
must have been used for transfer to canvas, is lost.

90 Head of Don Quixote

Tête de Don Quichotte—Tête d'homme

Panel: 33 by 24·5 (13 by 9⅝).

PROVENANCE: Boy; Ackermann; Thannhauser;
Schuler.

LITERATURE: *Cat. de la Vente Boy*, Versailles,
1905, No. 5; Klossowski, 62F and pl. 48; Fuchs,
166.

Lent by the Kunsthaus, Zürich

Probably painted in the early 1860s, and certainly
several years before the study in the Rijksmuseum
Kröller-Müller (see No. 91).

91 Head of Don Quixote

Tête de Don Quichotte

Canvas: 31·5 by 25 (12⅜ by 10).

PROVENANCE: Hoogendijk.

LITERATURE: *Cat. de la Vente Hoogendijk*,
Amsterdam, 1912, No. 20.

Lent by the Rijksmuseum Kröller-Müller, Otterlo

Painted about 1866–68.

92 Don Quixote and Sancho Panza

PLATE 20C

Panel: 36 by 52 (14⅛ by 20½). R.l.c.: *h.D.*

PROVENANCE: Nadar (?); Hazard; Barbizon
House; Sadler; Petit; Knoedler; Michael M. van
Beuren.

LITERATURE: *Cat. de la Vente Hazard*, Paris, 1919,
No. 101; Klossowski, 52; Sadleir, pl. 4; Fuchs, ill.
2, on the dedication leaf.

*Lent by Mr and Mrs Archbold van Beuren, Newport,
R.I.*

A very closely related charcoal study, presumably
the *première pensée* for this monochrome, is in the
collection of the late Jakob Goldschmidt (see
No. 227). The Goncourts note in their *Journal*
(21 Aug. 1893), on the occasion of a visit to Nadar,
that they saw there '*une spirituelle grisaille de
Daumier, représentant un Don Quichotte ridicule*'.
Again, on 24 Nov. 1895, they note that this picture
'*n'a guère dépassé une centaine de francs*' at the sale
of Nadar's collection. As no other Don Quixote
painting which can be described as a grisaille is so
far known, this picture might well be the one owned
by Daumier's friend Nadar.

93 Don Quixote reading

*Don Quichotte lisant [un roman de la
chevalerie]*

Canvas: 78·5 by 63·5 (30⅞ by 25). L.r.c.: *h.D.*

PROVENANCE: Paris art market (*c.* 1916); Gwendoline E. Davies.

LITERATURE: Maison, in *Burl. Mag.*, April 1954,
p. 106, No. 7 and Fig. 15.

Lent by the National Museum of Wales, Cardiff

Study, on a larger scale, for the painting in the
National Gallery of Victoria, Melbourne (see No.
94).

94 Don Quixote reading

*Don Quichotte lisant [un roman de la
chevalerie]—Don Quichotte dans un
fauteuil* PLATE 36

Panel: 35 by 26 (13¾ by 10¼).

PROVENANCE: Lemaire; G. Bernheim; A. Reid;
Rinder.

EXHIBITIONS: Durand-Ruel, 1878 (8); *La Caricature*, 1888 (367); Beaux-Arts, 1901 (51); Basle,
Société des Beaux-Arts, *Peinture française*, 1921
(50).

LITERATURE: Alexandre, p. 373; *Kunst und Künstler*, 1922, p. 345; Klossowski, 37; Fontainas, 13;
Fuchs, 160; Escholier, 1930, pl. 13; Fleischmann/
Sachs, pl. 61; Lassaigne, pl. 160; *Formes et Couleurs*,
1945, I, p. 35; Maison, in *Burl. Mag.*, April 1954,
p. 106 and Fig. 16; Adhémar, pl. 170 ('*vers 1868*');
Schweicher, pl. 61.

Lent by the National Gallery of Victoria, Melbourne

Possibly painted not later than 1863, although Adhémar reproduces this panel as one of Daumier's last paintings.

95 Don Quixote and Sancho Panza

Panel: 32·3 by 24·2 (12¾ by 9½). L.l.c.: *h.D.*

PROVENANCE: Aubry; Wisselingh; Burrell.

EXHIBITIONS: *La Caricature*, 1888 (363); Glasgow, *International Exhibition*, 1901 (1342); London, Tate Gallery, *Loan Exhibition of the Burrell Collection*, 1924 (10); Arts Council travelling exhibition, *French Paintings of the 19th Century from the Burrell Collection*, 1950 (19).

LITERATURE: *Cat. de la Vente P. A*[ubry]., Paris, 1897, No. 2; Klossowski, 43 and pl. 42; Fuchs, notes with 162 and 304b; Adhémar, pl. 168, in colour ('*vers* 1868').

Lent by the Corporation of Glasgow, Burrell Collection

A very similar second version, lighter in colour and on a smaller scale, is in the Herman Schulman Collection, New York. There are also several related compositions, some of them of doubtful authenticity.

96 Don Quixote

Oil on board: 11·8 by 12·2 (4⅝ by 4¾).

Lent by Monsieur Pierre Granville, Paris

This unrecorded little study corresponds in all essential details with the central figure in the drawing in the Musée des Beaux-Arts, Rheims (see No. 228).

97 Don Quixote and Sancho Panza

FRONTISPIECE

Panel: 100 by 81 (39½ by 32).

PROVENANCE: Vollard; P. Rosenberg; Bignou; Reid & Lefevre; S. Courtauld.

EXHIBITIONS: Beaux-Arts, 1901 (89); Galerie Rosenberg, 1907 (32); Basle, Société des Beaux-Arts, *Peinture Française*, 1921 (52); Lefevre Galleries, 1927 (5); on loan to the Tate Gallery, 1927; New York, 1930 (51); London, Royal Academy, *French Art, 1200–1900*, 1932 (376); London, Tate Gallery, *Samuel Courtauld Memorial Exhibition*, 1948 (20).

LITERATURE: Klossowski, 51 and pl. 43; Fuchs, 165; Lassaigne, pl. 155; *Commemorative Cat. of the Exhibition of French Art at the Royal Academy, 1932*, 1933, No. 327 and pl. 104; *Apollo*, 1947,

p. 57; D. Cooper, Cat. of the Courtauld Collection, 1954, No. 20 and pl. 3.

Lent by the Courtauld Institute of Art, London

No finished version of this composition is known. An imitation on canvas exists, which measures 41·5 by 33 cm.

98 Don Quixote and Sancho Panza

Don Quichotte courant sur les moutons

PLATE 21B

Canvas: 56 by 84 (22 by 33⅛). L.l.c.: *h. Daumier.*

PROVENANCE: Bureau; Knoedler.

EXHIBITIONS: Durand-Ruel, 1878 (13); Paris, *Exposition Centennale*, 1889 (232); Beaux-Arts, 1901 (15); New York, 1930 (50); Orangerie, 1934 (37); Chicago, Art Institute, *A Century of Progress*, 1934 (182); Amsterdam, Stedelijk Museum, *Honderd Jaar Fransche Kunst*, 1938 (89); New York, World's Fair, 1940 (257); San Francisco, *Golden Gate Exhibition*, 1946 (257); New Haven, Yale University, *Pictures collected by Alumni*, 1956 (57).

LITERATURE: Alexandre, pp. 346 and 373; Klossowski, 47; *Cat. de la Vente P. Bureau*, Paris, 1927, No. 102; *Apollo*, May 1928, p. 215, and 1930, p. 453; *Magazine of Art* (Washington), December 1930, p. 709; Fuchs, 154 and pl. 155; Escholier, 1930, pl. 28; Fleischmann/Sachs, pl. 9; Lassaigne, pl. 158; *Art News* (N.Y.), November 1946, p. 38; Adhémar, pl. 163 ('*vers* 1866'); Schweicher, pl. 62; Cherpin, in *Gazette des Beaux-Arts*, May/June 1958, p. 332 and Fig. 1.

Lent by Mr and Mrs Charles S. Payson, New York

The first idea for this famous picture was undoubtedly the drawing in the Roger-Marx Collection (see No. 229). As is usual in Daumier's work, the composition of the painting corresponds exactly with the sketch. Between that drawing and the final painting, there are, however, two important painted studies. The first is presumably the somewhat sketchy painting of the complete composition (40 by 62·5 cm.) in the Hugh Lane Bequest (National Gallery, London, at present in Ireland); here the unfinished figure of Sancho Panza is indifferent and probably did not satisfy the artist, and he painted a large version of this detail, essentially a brush drawing on canvas (71 by 62 cm.; now in a private collection in Paris). The finished painting remained with the artist for a number of years until, in October 1876, Mme Bureau acquired it for Frs. 1500. Daumier noted the sale in his account book for that year, calling the picture *Don Quichotte courant sur les moutons.*

99 Don Quixote in the Mountains

Don Quichotte dans les montagnes—Don Quichotte et la mule morte

Panel: 23·5 by 45 (9¼ by 17¾).

PROVENANCE: Saucède; Hoogendijk.

LITERATURE: *Cat. de la Vente A. Saucède*, Paris, 1879, No. 9; *Cat. de la Vente Hoogendijk*, Amsterdam, 1912, No. 19; Klossowski, 39A; Fuchs, mentioned in note on 158.

Lent by the Rijksmuseum Kröller-Müller, Otterlo

Earlier version of the painting in the Metropolitan Museum, New York (Adhémar: '*vers* 1868'). The charcoal study for this composition (see No. 230) shows that Daumier originally intended it to be in the inverse sense; on the back of the same paper, however, he reversed it and squared it for transfer.

100 Don Quixote on a white Horse

Don Quichotte sur un cheval blanc

PLATE 20B

Panel: 40 by 31 (15¾ by 12¼).

PROVENANCE: Vollard; Cassirer.

EXHIBITIONS: New York, Knoedler Galleries, *Loan Exhibition of the Collection of Erich Maria Remarque*, 1943 (5); on loan first to the Metropolitan Museum, New York, and subsequently to the Kunsthaus, Zürich, 1958–60.

LITERATURE: Klossowski, 54.

Lent by Mr Erich Maria Remarque, Ascona

A very late sketch, probably dating from 1868–70. No finished version of this composition is known.

Water-Colours and Drawings

101 The Prodigal Son

L'enfant prodigue—Le bon Samaritain— L'aveugle et le paralytique

Pen and wash: 20·5 by 11·5 (8⅛ by 4½).

PROVENANCE: Lemaire; Barbazanges; Reid & Lefevre; Gwendoline E. Davies.

EXHIBITION: Lefevre Galleries, 1922 (5).

LITERATURE: Klossowski, 7A.

Lent by the National Museum of Wales, Cardiff

The subject of this drawing is not certain; several studies for the same composition are known, five of them in the National Gallery of Art, Washington (Rosenwald Collection). Although they were obviously made as studies for a painting, no such picture is known to exist.

102 The Destruction of Sodom (?)

La destruction de Sodom—L'émeute— Scène de la révolution

Charcoal, water-colour and gouache: 58 by 43 (22⅞ by 17). Inscribed by Arsène Alexandre: *Esquisse de H. Daumier provenant de son atelier de Valmondois et acquise de Mme. Vve. Daumier en 1891 (février).*

PROVENANCE: Mme Daumier; Alexandre; Davigneau; Mrs W. F. R. Weldon.

LITERATURE: *Cat. de la Vente Arsène Alexandre*, Paris, 1903, No. 129; Klossowski, 109; *Ars Graphica*, pl. 10; Fuchs, 243; K. T. Parker, *Cat. of the Collection of Drawings in the Ashmolean Museum*, Oxford, 1938, I, No. 572 and pl. CLV; Adhémar, pl. 38 ('1848/50').

Lent by the Ashmolean Museum, Oxford

The subject of this drawing remains doubtful; it may, however, be a preliminary study for some revolutionary scene, intended as an illustration for Henry Martin's *Histoire de France*. The Pushkin Museum, Moscow, owns a very finished drawing, *Camille Desmoulins au Palais Royal*, of approximately the same dimensions and in the same technique, which is known to have been intended as an illustration for that work.

103 The Bathers

Les baigneurs

Black chalk, partly over pencil, and water-colour: 21 by 18·9 (8¼ by 7½). L.r.c.: *h.D.*

PROVENANCE: Lucas; on loan to the Baltimore Museum of Art since 1934.

LITERATURE: *Art News* (N.Y.), December 1951, p. 38; Maison, *Drawings*, ill. 41.

Lent by the Maryland Institute, Baltimore, Lucas Collection, by courtesy of the Baltimore Museum of Art.

Drawn about 1860–62.

104 Man on Horseback

Cavalier   PLATE 27C

Pen and ink: 20·9 by 26·5 (8¼ by 10½).

PROVENANCE: Roger Marx.

EXHIBITIONS: Galerie Dru ,1927 (50); Orangerie, 1934 (171); Leicester Galleries, 1936 (43); Albertina, 1936 (7); Zürich, Kunsthaus, *Von David zu Millet*, 1937 (31); Philadelphia, 1937 (47); Bibliothèque Nationale, 1958 (319).

LITERATURE: Fuchs, p. 29, ill. 41; Fleischmann/ Sachs, embossed on the front cover; Lassaigne, pl. 115; R. Lejeune, *Daumier*, Zürich, 1945, repr. on the title-page; Maison, *Drawings*, ill. 59.

Lent by Monsieur Claude Roger-Marx, Paris

105 Man on Horseback

Cavalier   PLATE 27B

Pen and ink: 19·4 by 16·5 (7⅝ by 6½). L.l.c.: *h.D.*

PROVENANCE: Theo van Gogh.

EXHIBITIONS: Amsterdam, Stedelijk Museum, *Daumier en zijn Tijd*, 1920 (13); Amsterdam Stedelijk Museum, *De verzameling van Theo van Gogh*, 1953 (20).

LITERATURE: Maison, in *Burl. Mag.*, June 1956, Fig. 24; Maison, *Drawings*, ill. 61.

Lent by Ir V. W. Van Gogh, from his collection in the Stedelijk Museum, Amsterdam

106 Study for the Relief 'Les Emigrants'

Etude pour le bas-relief 'Les Emigrants'

Black chalk, pen and wash: 25 by 37 (9⅞ by 14⅝). L.r.c.: *h.D.*

PROVENANCE: Roger Marx.

EXHIBITIONS: Galerie Dru, 1927 (45); Orangerie, 1934 (163); Leicester Galleries, 1936 (45); Albertina, 1936 (4); Zürich, Kunsthaus, *Von David zu Millet*, 1937 (26); Paris, Galerie Sagot-Le Garrec, *Daumier Sculpteur*, 1957 (78); Bibliothèque Nationale, 1958 (102).

LITERATURE: Fuchs, 327b; Lassaigne, pl. 112; Adhémar, pl. 44 ('*vers* 1848/49').

Lent by Monsieur Claude Roger-Marx, Paris

Daumier's only known preparatory drawing for a work of sculpture. The well-known relief corresponds in all essential details with this study.

107 A Convoy of Prisoners

Un convoi de prisonniers—Les fugitifs

Black chalk and wash: 13·8 by 24 (5⅞ by 9½). L.l.: *h.D.* Verso a study of a male head in pen and water-colour.

PROVENANCE: Wasset (1869).

LITERATURE: Martine-Marotte, pl. 35; Fuchs, 266a.

Lent by the Ecole des Beaux-Arts, Paris.

108 The Kiss

Le baiser—Adam et Eve—Nymphe surprise

Brown charcoal on prepared paper: 30 by 24·9 (11¾ by 9⅞).

PROVENANCE: Babcock; W. Gay.

LITERATURE: P. Leprieur, *Les Musés de France*, 1913, p. 36; Klossowski, 20B; *Ars Graphica*, pl. 47;

Martine-Marotte, pl. 2; Fuchs, 265b; Fleischmann/
Sachs, pl. 3; Lassaigne, pl. 118; *L'Art et les
Artistes*, 1938, p. 60; C. Roger-Marx, *Daumier*,
1938, p. 57; Escholier, 1938, p. 103; Adhémar,
Drawings, pl. 8; Adhémar, pl. 55 ('*vers* 1849/50').
Lent by the Musée du Louvre, Paris

109 Three gossiping Women

Les trois commères

Pencil and charcoal: 23·2 by 29 (9⅛ by 11⅜). L.r.c.:
h.D.

PROVENANCE: Alexandre; Pra; Strolin; Grange.

EXHIBITION: Orangerie, 1934 (75).

LITERATURE: *Cat. de la Vente Arsène Alexandre*,
Paris, 1903, No. 119; Klossowski, 291B; *Cat. de la
Vente A. Pra*, Paris, 1938, No. 5; Maison, *Drawings*,
ill. 17.

Lent by Mr and Mrs Leigh B. Block, Chicago

A very similar drawing in charcoal, pen and ink is
in the Ionides Collection at the Victoria & Albert
Museum and a water-colour sketch, which is almost
identical with the present drawing, was formerly in
the Bureau Collection. These drawings, as well as
the final water-colour version (see No. 110) are
very close to a lithograph (Delteil 2263) published
in *Charivari* in 1852 but are not, however, studies
for it.

110 Three gossiping Women

Les trois commères   PLATE 25C

Black chalk, pen and water-colour: 26 by 18
(10¼ by 7⅛). L.l.c.: *h. Daumier.*

PROVENANCE: Petit.

EXHIBITIONS: Durand-Ruel, 1878 (201); Bibliothèque Nationale, 1958 (311).

LITERATURE: Alexandre, p. 377; Maison, *Drawings*, ill. 19.

Lent by Wildenstein & Company, New York

See note on No. 109.

111 The young Mother

La jeune mère   PLATE 24H

Black chalk, pen and wash: 17·2 by 12·7 (6¾ by 5).

Lent by Monsieur H. Stuart de Clèves, Paris

Unrecorded first version of the slightly larger
water-colour (reproduced Fuchs 233a), now in a
private collection in Paris. According to family
tradition, these drawings represent Mme Bureau,
with her baby son Paul, who owned the finest

collection of works by Daumier assembled in the
nineteenth century.

112 Mother and Child

Mère et enfant   PLATE 24G

Charcoal on light buff paper: 30·8 by 23·5 (12⅛
by 9¼).

PROVENANCE: Babcock; Bradlee.

LITERATURE: Maison, *Drawings*, ill. 15.

Lent by Monsieur César M. de Hauke, Paris

William P. Babcock (1826–99), an almost forgotten
American painter in Paris, was very close to the
Barbizon painters and especially to Millet. It was
most probably through this staunch friend of
Daumier that Babcock became acquainted with
the artist, from whom he acquired this drawing.
Only a very few studies in this clear and strong
charcoal technique are known (see also No. 138).

113 The Grandmother

La grand'mère

Pen and wash: 14·6 by 12·8 (5¾ by 5). L.r.c.: *h.D.*
Verso a study of a man's head.

PROVENANCE: Doisteau; Rosenwald.

EXHIBITION: Philadelphia, Free Library, *Lithographs and Drawings by Honoré Daumier lent by
Lessing J. Rosenwald*, 1930 (199).

LITERATURE: *Cat. de la Vente F. Doisteau*, Paris,
1928, No. 7; Adhémar, *Drawings*, pl. 43 ('*vers*
1848').

*Lent by the National Gallery of Art, Washington,
Rosenwald Collection.*

114 Little Boy running

Le jeune coureur

Black chalk and wash: 15 by 23 (5⅞ by 9). L.l.c.:
h.D.

PROVENANCE: Bureau; Thannhauser; Rosenwald.

EXHIBITIONS: Beaux-Arts, 1901 (158); Philadelphia, Free Library, *Lithographs and Drawings by
Honoré Daumier lent by Lessing J. Rosenwald*, 1930
(201); Philadelphia, 1937 (49).

LITERATURE: *Cat. de la Vente P. Bureau*, Paris,
1927, No. 51; Fuchs, p. 59, ill. 86; Escholier, 1930,
pl. 71; Maison, *Drawings*, ill. 28.

*Lent by the National Gallery of Art, Washington,
Rosenwald Collection*

115 A Peasant Woman putting Bread in the Oven

Paysanne enfournant du pain

Black chalk, slightly heightened with white, on bluish buff paper: 29·8 by 42·2 (11¾ by 16⅝).

PROVENANCE: Régereau; Vollard; Cassirer; Koenigs.

EXHIBITION: Beaux-Arts, 1901 (248).

LITERATURE: Klossowski, 245; Maison, *Drawings*, ill. 25.

Lent from a Private Collection, Heemstede.

116 Man carrying a Bucket

Le porteur d'eau—Homme de peine

Charcoal on blueish paper: 27·9 by 20 (11 by 7⅞). Verso a study in the same medium, of a man guiding the steps of a child (*Le premier bain*).

PROVENANCE: Lemaire; Barbazanges; Reid & Lefevre; Anderson.

EXHIBITIONS: Beaux-Arts, 1901 (485); Lefevre Galleries, 1922 (1).

LITERATURE: Klossowski, 236A; Sadleir, pl. 19; Maison, in *Burl. Mag.*, June 1956, p. 200 and Fig. 16.

Lent by the British Museum, London.

Study for the painting *Le porteur d'eau* in the Barnes Foundation, Merion (Pa.).

117 Family Scene   PLATE 24C

Monsieur, Madame et Bébé—Maternité

Black chalk and water-colour: 18 by 20 (7⅛ by 7⅞). L.r.c.: *h. Daumier*.

PROVENANCE: Marx; Bernheim; Pra; Kapferer; Wildenstein.

EXHIBITIONS: Beaux-Arts, 1901 (119); Galerie Dru, 1927 (11); Orangerie, 1934 (55).

LITERATURE: Klossowski, 315A; *Cat. de la Vente Albert Pra*, Paris, 1938, No. 7; Adhémar, *Drawings*, pl. 32 ('vers 1862'); Adhémar, pl. 76 ('1855/60'); Maison, *Drawings*, ill. 35.

Lent by the Phillips Collection, Washington

118 Two Dogs fighting

Deux chiens se mordant   PLATE 27A

Charcoal: 14 by 19·7 (5½ by 7¾).

Lent by Dr Günter Busch, Bremen

This unrecorded little drawing is very close to the main detail of a lithograph published in *Charivari*

in 1856 (Delteil 2749). There an Englishman, complete with umbrella, is seen acting as amateur umpire while two continental nations—represented by the two dogs—go for each other.

119 Landscape

Paysage—Paysage au gros arbre

Pen and wash: 29·8 by 41·9 (11¾ by 16½).

PROVENANCE: Roger Marx.

EXHIBITIONS: Galerie Dru, 1927 (79); Orangerie, 1934 (179); Bibliothèque Nationale, 1958 (115).

LITERATURE: Fuchs, 228b; Adhémar, *Drawings*, pl. 14; Adhémar, pl. 70 ('vers 1852'); Maison, *Drawings*, ill. 53.

Lent by Monsieur Claude Roger-Marx, Paris

While the artist has used landscape for the setting of a few of his paintings and drawings, it was invariably the human figure which was given all the prominence. Pure landscape paintings by Daumier do not exist, while in all only three landscape drawings are known; the other two are in the same collection as the present study.

120 Domino-players   PLATE 24B

Joueurs de domino—La partie de dominos

Pen and wash over black chalk: 17 by 25 (6¾ by 9⅞). L.l.c.: *h.D.*

PROVENANCE: Caresse; Geoffroy-Dechaume; Durand-Ruel (?); Gerstenberg.

EXHIBITIONS: Durand-Ruel, 1878 (164); *La Caricature*, 1888 (383); Matthiesen, 1926 (130).

LITERATURE: Alexandre, p. 377; *Cat. de la Vente Geoffroy-Dechaume*, Paris, 1893, No. 59; *Drucke der Marées Gesellschaft*, IX, *Daumier*, Munich, 1918, pl. 10; *Ars Graphica*, pl. 37; Fuchs, 215a; Fleischmann/Sachs, pl. 82; Adhémar, *Drawings*, pl. 41 ('vers 1862').

Lent by Dr Fritz Nathan, Zürich

A very small sketch for this composition, in pen and wash, is in the collection of Mrs S. Dreyfus, New York.

121 Study of a Man reading

La lecture—Le lecteur

Pen and wash: 14·5 by 11·5 (5¾ by 4½). R.l.c.: *h.D.*

PROVENANCE: v.d. Heydt; de Hauke.

LITERATURE: W. Hugelshofer, *Dessins et Aquarelles de Maîtres Français du XIXe siècle en Suisse*, Portfolio I de la Société Holbein, Basle, 1927, No. 8.

Lent by Frau Marianne Feilchenfeldt, Zürich

122 A Writer

Un écrivain—La rédaction du placet—
Le dessinateur   PLATE 23J

Pencil, pen and wash over charcoal: 12·1 by 18·5
(4¾ by 7¼). L.l.c.: *h.D.*

PROVENANCE: Hazard; Pra.

EXHIBITIONS: Orangerie, 1934 (86); Buenos
Aires, Museo Nacional de Bellas Artes, *Dibujos
siglos XIX y XX*, 1959 (16).

LITERATURE: *Cat. de la Vente Hazard*, Paris, 1919,
I, No. 319; Fuchs, Suppl. p. 2, ill. 2b; *Cat. de la
Vente A. Pra*, Paris, 1938, No. 4.

Lent by Dr Zdenko Bruck, Buenos Aires

Study for the painting now with Wildenstein &
Company, New York (see No. 38).

123 Man lighting his Pipe

Fumeur allumant sa pipe

Pen and brown wash: 13·5 by 11 (5¼ by 4¼).

PROVENANCE: Simon.

EXHIBITION: Bibliothèque Nationale, 1958 (175).

LITERATURE: *Cat. de la Vente Victor Simon*, Paris,
1939, No. 40; Maison, in *Gazette des Beaux-Arts*,
May/June 1958, p. 347, Fig. 7.

Lent by Monsieur Roger Leybold, Paris

The head of a man smoking, the central figure in
the water-colour *Chasseurs se chauffant*, in the
Esnault-Pelterie Collection, is almost identical.

124 Studies of a Man smoking and a Man reading

Le fumeur et le lecteur—Au café

Pen and ink over charcoal: 12·5 by 20 (4⅞ by 7⅞).

PROVENANCE: Gallimard; Brame.

Lent by Mr Edwin C. Vogel, New York

125 Man lighting his Pipe

Le fumeur allumant sa pipe

Black chalk, pen and wash: 26·5 by 20 (10½ by 7⅞).
L.l.c.: *h.D.*

PROVENANCE: Bureau; Stonborough; Stern.

EXHIBITIONS: Durand-Ruel, 1878 (114); Beaux-
Arts, 1901 (132).

LITERATURE: Alexandre, p. 377; Klossowski, 357;
Cat. de la Vente P. Bureau, Paris, 1927, No. 69;
Fuchs, 325; Escholier, 1930, pl. 76; Cat. of the
Stonborough Sale, New York, 1940, No. 39;
Scheiwiller, pl. XV.

Lent by Mr James H. Lockhart, Jr., Geneseo, N.Y.

126 The good Friends

Les bons amis—Les deux amis   PLATE 25B

Pen and white chalk over pencil, washed with
water-colour and white gouache: 22·8 by 30 (9 by
11¾). L.r.c.: *h. Daumier.*

PROVENANCE: Lucas; on loan to the Baltimore
Museum of Art since 1934.

EXHIBITION: Galerie Rosenberg, 1907 (11).

LITERATURE: *Art News* (N.Y.), December 1951,
p. 38; Maison, *Drawings*, ill. 39.

*Lent by the Maryland Institute, Baltimore, Lucas
Collection, by courtesy of the Baltimore Museum of
Art.*

Probably bought by M. Lucas from the artist on the
occasion of one of his visits to Daumier's studio in
1864. This may well be the approximate date of the
drawing.

127 La Politique   PLATE 25A

Pen and water-colour wash: 37 by 28 (14⅝ by 11).
L.l.c.: *h. Daumier.*

PROVENANCE: Aubry; Camentron; Durand-Ruel;
Gerstenberg; Matthiesen.

EXHIBITIONS: Beaux-Arts, 1901 (195); Galerie
Rosenberg, 1907 (2); London, National Gallery,
French Art of the 19th Century, 1943 (26).

LITERATURE: *Cat. de la Vente P. A[ubry].*, Paris,
1897, No. 41; *Kunst und Künstler*, 1911, p. 185;
Klossowski, 262 and pl. 104; Escholier, 1923,
p. 169; *Ars Graphica*, pl. 34; Sadleir, pl. 52; Fuchs,
217a; Lassaigne, pl. 51; Cassou, pl. 20 (as being in
the Reinhart Coll.); Schweicher, pl. 11; Maison, in
Burl. Mag., May 1956, p. 165 and Fig. 51; Ziller,
pl. 100; Maison, *Drawings*, ill. 40.

Lent by Herr Albert Ch. Nussbaumer, Lugano.

There is a second version of this drawing, now in the
collection of Dr Oskar Reinhart, Winterthur; it is
in black chalk washed with blue-ish water-colour
and was undoubtedly made with the help of a
tracing of the present drawing.

128 A last Word

Un dernier mot　　　　　　　PLATE 24D

Pen and wash over black chalk: 17 by 21·5 (6¾ by 8½). L.r.c.: *h. Daumier.*

PROVENANCE: Tavernier; Darrasse; Nathan.

LITERATURE: *Cat. de la Vente Tavernier*, Paris, 1900, No. 112; Klossowski, 408; Maison, in *Gazette des Beaux-Arts*, May/June 1958, p. 350, Fig. 10; Maison, *Drawings*, ill. 38.

Lent by Mr and Mrs Lazarus Phillips, Montreal

129 Head of a Man

Tête d'homme

Pen and ink: 16·5 by 12 (6½ by 4¾). Centre right: *h.D.*

PROVENANCE: Vita; Bignou; de Hauke; Kraushaar; Schnackenberg.

EXHIBITION: Lefevre Galleries, 1927 (18).

LITERATURE: Fuchs, 177d; Maison, *Drawings*, ill. 1.

Lent by the Wadsworth Atheneum, Hartford, Conn.

An unsigned copy of this drawing, on a much larger scale, passed through a German auction sale in 1949.

130 A Man shouting

Homme poussant un cri

Pen and wash: 8 by 7·5 (3⅛ by 2⅞). L.r.c.: *h.D.*

PROVENANCE: Reid & Lefevre.

EXHIBITION: On loan to the Tate Gallery, 1930.

LITERATURE: Maison, *Drawings*, ill. 99.

Lent by the Corporation of Glasgow, Burrell Collection

131 A Man laughing

Le rieur　　　　　　　PLATE 23H

Pen and wash over black chalk: 12 by 9·5 (4¾ by 3¾). L.r.: *h.D.*

PROVENANCE: Bureau; P. M. Turner.

EXHIBITIONS: Beaux-Arts, 1901 (154); London, Royal Academy, *French Art, 1200–1900*, 1932

(947); Paris, Palais National des Arts, *Chefs d'œuvre de l'Art français*, 1937 (627).

LITERATURE: Klossowski, 270; *Cat. de la Vente P. Bureau*, Paris, 1927, No. 46; Fuchs, 177c; *Commemorative Cat. of the Exhibition of French Art at the Royal Academy, 1932*, 1933, No. 813; Huyghe and Jaccottet, *Le Dessin français au XIXe siècle*, 1948, pl. 52; Schweicher, pl. 12; Maison, *Drawings*, ill. 10.

Lent by the Fitzwilliam Museum, Cambridge

132 Study of a Man's Head

Etude de tête d'homme　　　　　　　PLATE 23F

Black chalk and charcoal, varnished with gum arabic, laid down on board: 23 by 18 (9 by 7⅛). L.r.: *h.D.*

PROVENANCE: Mme Thesmar (?).

LITERATURE: *Cat. of a Sale at the Salle Drouot*, Paris, 9 June 1949, No. 25; Maison, in *Burl. Mag.*, April 1954, p. 106 and Fig. 10; Adhémar, note on pl. 39; Maison, *Drawings*, ill. 11.

Lent from a Private Collection

Study of the head of the central figure in the painting *La Famille sur la Barricade*, in Prague (see also No. 39). The drawing is laid down on a piece of board on the reverse of which is pasted part of an issue of the journal *La Commune*, which appeared in 1848–49 only. This may well be the approximate date of the drawing.

133 Study of a terrified Woman

Etude d'une femme épouvantée

Charcoal and pencil: 20·3 by 23·4 (8 by 9¼).

PROVENANCE: Roger Marx; Carstairs; R. Allerton.

LITERATURE: *Jahrbuch der Jungen Kunst* (Leipzig), 1924, p. 432; Maison, *Drawings*, ill. 20.

Lent by the Art Institute of Chicago

134 Study of a seated Man

Etude d'homme assis

Pen and ink: 14·4 by 12·2 (5⅝ by 4⅞).

PROVENANCE: Pothey (?); Rossignol; Robert Grange.

LITERATURE: A. Pothey, *La Muette*, Paris, 1870, p. 6 (with the caption '*Un membre de l'Institut*');

Maison, in *Gazette des Beaux-Arts*, May/June 1958, p. 347 and Fig. 6.

Lent by the Staatsgalerie Stuttgart, Graphische Sammlung

See note on No. 142.

135 Heads of two Men

Têtes de deux hommes

Pen and ink: 14 by 19 (5½ by 7½).
PROVENANCE: Blot; Lindon; Rewald; Berggruen.
EXHIBITIONS: Middletown (Conn.), Davison Art Centre, Wesleyan University, *Symposium on the Graphic Arts* (repr. on the cover of the cat.), 1955; Los Angeles, Municipal Art Gallery, *The Collection of Mr and Mrs John Rewald*, 1959 (22).
LITERATURE: Cat. of the J. Rewald Sale, London, 1960, No. 23.
Lent by Mr and Mrs Matthew Futter, New York.

136 Heads of two laughing Men

Têtes de deux hommes riant　　　PLATE 23 I

Pencil, black chalk and wash: 25 by 22 (9⅞ by 5⅝).
PROVENANCE: A. Rouart; Cassirer.
Lent by Herr Hermann J. Abs, Frankfurt-on-Main

137 Two male Heads

Deux têtes

Pen and brown ink: 12·2 by 17 (4¾ by 6¾). L.l.: *h.D.*
Lent by Monsieur G. Heim-Gairac, Paris

An almost identical drawing is in the Museum of Fine Arts, Budapest.

138 Two male Heads

Deux têtes d'hommes

Charcoal: 16·7 by 15 (6⅝ by 5⅞). L.l.c.: *h.D.*
PROVENANCE: Koenigs.
EXHIBITIONS: Rotterdam, Museum Boymans, *Verzameling Koenigs*, 1935–36 (17); Albertina, 1936 (25).
Lent by the Museum Boymans-van Beuningen, Rotterdam

See note on No. 112.

139 Three Studies of male Heads

Trois études de têtes d'hommes

Black chalk, pen and wash: 11 by 17·1 (4⅜ by 6¾).
Lower centre: *h.D.*
PROVENANCE: Cahen; P. M. Turner; Reid & Lefevre.
EXHIBITIONS: London, Royal Academy, *French Art, 1200–1900*, 1932 (917); Leicester Galleries, 1936 (66); Oxford, Maison Française, *Quelques artistes français de la collection P. M. Turner*, 1950 (9).
LITERATURE: *Cat. de la 1ᵉ Vente Cahen*, Paris, 1929, No. 19; *Commemorative Cat. of the Exh. of French Art at the Royal Academy, 1932*, 1933, No. 808; New York, *Pictures on Exhibit*, April 1953, p. 33.
Lent by Smith College Museum of Art, Northampton, Mass.

140 Three male Heads

Trois têtes d'hommes

Black chalk and water-colour: 11 by 22 (4⅜ by 8⅝).
L.l.c.: *h.D.*
PROVENANCE: Liebermann; Riezler; de Hauke.
EXHIBITION: Matthiesen, 1926 (89).
LITERATURE: *Kunst und Künstler*, VI, 1908, p. 195; Fuchs, 209a.
Lent by Mr Gregoire Tarnopol, New York

141 The Barrel-organ

L'Orgue de Barbarie　　　PLATE 27D

Black chalk, pen and water-colour: 34 by 26 (13⅜ by 10¼). L.l.c.: *h. Daumier*.
PROVENANCE: Jacquette.
LITERATURE: Klossowski, 220 and pl. 85; Escholier, 1923, plate facing p. 10, and 1930, pl. 69; Sadleir, pl. 10; *Ars Graphica*, pl. XI; Martine-Marotte, pl. 7; Fuchs, 254; Fleischmann/Sachs, pl. 16; Lassaigne, pl. 151; Cassou, pl. 38; Adhémar, *Drawings*, pl. 48; Adhémar, pl. 142, in colour ('*vers* 1860'); Maison, *Drawings*, ill. 64.
Lent by the Musée du Petit Palais, Paris

Another version, partly unfinished, is in the Bührle Collection, Zürich.

142 Study of two Singers

Deux chanteurs: Ténor léger et Basse profonde

Pen and ink, lightly washed: 12·4 by 26 (4⅞ by 10¼). Inscribed by another hand.

PROVENANCE: Pothey (?); Rossignol; Robert Grange.

LITERATURE: A. Pothey, *La Muette*, Paris, 1870, pp. 7 and 8; Maison, in *Gazette des Beaux-Arts*, May/June 1958, p. 347 and Fig. 1.

Lent by the Staatsgalerie, Stuttgart, Graphische Sammlung

One of ten drawings by Daumier which were pasted, among others, into the original manuscript of Pothey's book (op. cit.) and were re-discovered several years ago. They are reproduced in the printed edition, in woodcut facsimile, in the inverse sense and are again reproduced in the same way in the literature on prints after Daumier. The two heads shown in the present drawing are reproduced singly in the printed edition of 1870 and subsequently throughout the literature (see also No. 134).

143 A Guitarist, singing

Un guitariste chantant

Charcoal, black chalk and wash: 18 by 12 (7⅛ by 4¾).

PROVENANCE: Vollard; Cassirer.

LITERATURE: Maison, in *Gazette des Beaux-Arts*, May/June 1958, pp. 349–50 and Fig. 9.

Lent by Frau Marianne Feilchenfeldt, Zürich

144 A Guitarist, singing

Le guitariste chantant   PLATE 27E

Pen and ink over charcoal: 30·5 by 16 (12 by 5⅞).

PROVENANCE: J. G. Lousada; Barbizon House; Falk.

EXHIBITION: London, Burlington Fine Arts Club, *Pictures, Drawings and Sculpture of the French School of the Last 100 Years*, 1922 (56).

LITERATURE: Maison, in *Gazette des Beaux-Arts*, May/June 1958, p. 348 and Fig. 8; Maison, *Drawings*, ill. 65.

Lent by Miss A. E. Hübler, Oxfordshire

145 A Violinist, singing   PLATE 27G

Le violiniste chantant—Chanteur des rues

Pen and wash: 28·6 by 20·6 (11¼ by 8⅛).

PROVENANCE: Bignou; Reid & Lefevre.

EXHIBITION: On loan to the Tate Gallery, 1929.

LITERATURE: Fuchs, note on 210b; Adhémar, pl. 149 ('*vers* 1864'); Maison, *Drawings*, ill. 66.

Lent by the Corporation of Glasgow, Burrell Collection

Replica (by Daumier) of a wash drawing of the same size in the Gerstenberg Collection.

146 A Mandolin player

Page jouant de la mandoline—Le guitariste

Black chalk over pen and ink and wash: 32·2 by 21·6 (12¾ by 8½).

PROVENANCE: E. Parsons (1923).

LITERATURE: G. Diehl, *Le Dessin Français au XIXe siècle*, 1950, pl. 83; Maison, in *Burl. Mag.*, June 1956, p. 200 and Fig. 18.

Lent by the British Museum, London

Although this drawing differs in several details from the painting *The Troubadour* lent by the Cleveland Museum of Art (see No. 64), it is undoubtedly a study connected with it.

147 The Music Lover   PLATE 27F

L'amateur de Musique—Le Concert

Pen and ink over charcoal: 37·5 by 33·5 (14⅝ by 13).

PROVENANCE: Lemaire; Barbazanges; Matthiesen; Hess; Koenigs.

EXHIBITIONS: Lefevre Galleries, 1922 (34); Matthiesen, 1926 (129); Rotterdam, Museum Boymans, *Van Ingres tot Seurat*, 1933–34 (37); Rotterdam, Museum Boymans, *Verzameling Koenigs*, 1935–36 (14); Albertina, 1936 (20); Zürich, Kunsthaus, *Von David zu Millet*, 1937 (46).

LITERATURE: Klossowski, 336B; *Cat. de la Vente F. H[ess].*, Lucerne, 1931, No. 15; Fuchs, 208c; Maison, *Drawings*, ill. 111.

Lent by the Museum Boymans-van Beuningen, Rotterdam.

A subject which must have occupied Daumier's thoughts for a long time. Several studies for the listener exist, as well as a pen and ink sketch for the pianist in the background (S. H. Marcy Collection, Beverly Hills). The most finished wash drawing of this subject, now lost, was in the Gerstenberg Collection.

148 Corot drawing at Ville d'Avray

Corot dessinant à Ville d'Avray—La lecture à l'ombre   PLATE 24A

Pen and ink over pencil, washed with water-colour: 17·2 by 19 (6¾ by 7½). L.r.c.: *h.D.*

PROVENANCE: P. Rosenberg.

EXHIBITION: Bibliothèque Nationale, 1958 (114).

LITERATURE: Cat. of a Sale at the Salle Drouot, Paris, 28 November 1934, No. 5; L. Réau, *Un Siècle d'Aquarelle*, 1942, p. 47; Maison, in *Burl. Mag.*, January 1954, p. 14 and Fig. 15.

Lent by Monsieur Maurice Loncle, Paris

Study for the larger wash drawing in the Metropolitan Museum, New York.

149 Visitors in an Artist's Studio

Visiteurs dans l'atelier d'un artiste

Black chalk and wash, heightened with white: 8·5 by 12·5 (3⅜ by 4⅞). R.l.c.: *h.D.*

PROVENANCE: Babcock.

Lent by the Museum of Fine Arts, Boston, Mass.

Study for the water-colour in the Montreal Museum of Fine Arts (see No. 151). A study on a larger scale is in the Museum Boymans-van Beuningen, Rotterdam (see No. 150).

150 Visitors in an Artist's Studio

Dans l'atelier d'un artiste—Les amateurs de peinture—Les collectionneurs

Charcoal and black chalk, lightly washed: 38 by 49·7 (15 by 19⅝).

PROVENANCE: Lemaire; Reid & Lefevre; Koenigs.

EXHIBITIONS: Lefevre Galleries, 1922 (6); Rotterdam, Museum Boymans, *Van Ingres tot Seurat*, 1933–34 (38); Rotterdam, Museum Boymans, *Verzameling Koenigs*, 1935–36 (15); Albertina, 1936 (40); Zürich, Kunsthaus, *Von David zu Millet*, 1937 (43).

LITERATURE: Klossowski, 364A.

Lent by the Museum Boymans-van Beuningen, Rotterdam

Study for the water-colour in the Museum of Fine Arts, Montreal (see No. 151). See also No. 149.

151 Visitors in an Artist's Studio

Visiteurs dans l'atelier d'un artiste   PLATE 24E

Pen and ink and water-colour, heightened with gouache: 35 by 44·3 (13¾ by 17⅜). L.l.c.: *h. Daumier.*

PROVENANCE: Wisselingh; W. R. Miller.

LITERATURE: Adhémar, pl. 93, in colour ('*vers 1856/65*').

Lent by the Montreal Museum of Fine Arts, Bequest of Mrs W. R. Miller

Probably about 1863. For the two studies for this composition, see Nos. 149 and 150. A closely related water-colour is in the Walters Art Gallery, Baltimore.

152 Study of a Painter

Un peintre   PLATE 24F

Charcoal, black chalk, pen and wash in ink and sepia, heightened with white gouache: 19·5 by 18·5 (7⅝ by 7¼). L.r.c.: *h.D.*

PROVENANCE: Bureau; Wildenstein; Grace R. Rogers; P. Rosenberg; Knoedler.

EXHIBITIONS: Durand-Ruel, 1878 (106); Beaux-Arts, 1901 (124).

LITERATURE: Alexandre, p. 376; Klossowski, 387; *Cat. de la Vente P. Bureau*, Paris, 1927, No. 59; Fuchs, 332a; Escholier, 1930, pl. 52; Cat. of the Grace Rainey Rogers Estate Sale, New York, 1943, No. 45; Maison, *Drawings*, ill. 114.

Lent by Mr and Mrs Charles S. Payson, New York

153 Three Connoisseurs looking at Raffet's Lithographs

Trois amateurs d'estampes devant les lithographies de Raffet—Devant une litho de Raffet

Black chalk, pen and wash and water-colour, heightened with red chalk and pastel: 26 by 31 (10¼ by 12¼). L.l.: *h. Daumier.*

PROVENANCE: Giacomelli; Leclerc; Isaac de Camondo.

EXHIBITION: Durand-Ruel, 1878 (148).

LITERATURE: Alexandre, p. 376; *Cat. de la Vente H. Giacomelli*, Paris, 1905, No. 75; Klossowski, 376; Sadleir, pl. 31; *Ars Graphica*, pl. 8; Martine-Marotte, pl. 14; Fuchs, 245b; Fleischmann/Sachs,

pl. 55; Lassaigne, pl. 68; Escholier, 1938, p. 5; Adhémar, pl. 136 ('*vers* 1863/65').
Lent by the Musée du Louvre, Paris

This water-colour was very probably commissioned by Giacomelli, an admirer of Raffet (1804–60) and the author of the catalogue of his lithographs. The print which the three *amateurs* are admiring is *La Revue Nocturne*, one of Raffet's best works.

154 Study of a seated Man
Etude d'homme assis

Black chalk and water-colour: 21·2 by 28 (8⅜ by 11). L.l.: *h.D.*
PROVENANCE: Groult.
Lent by Mr Francis Matthiesen, London

One of several studies, in reverse, for the figure of the *Amateur* in the water-colour now in the Metropolitan Museum of Art, New York (see also No. 155).

155 The Collector
L'amateur

Charcoal, chalks and wash: 53·5 by 41·7 (21⅛ by 16⅜). L.l.c.: *h. Daumier à Cléophas.*
PROVENANCE: Doucet (?); Cassirer; Koenigs.
EXHIBITIONS: Matthiesen, 1926 (88); Rotterdam, Museum Boymans, *Van Ingres tot Seurat*, 1933–34 (36); Basle, Kunsthalle, *Meisterzeichnungen französischer Künstler von Ingres bis Cézanne*, 1935 (82); Rotterdam, Museum Boymans, *Verzameling Koenigs*, 1935–36 (13); Albertina, 1936 (19); Zürich, Kunsthaus, *Von David zu Millet*, 1937 (44).
LITERATURE: Klossowski, 377/377a; Fuchs, 331b; Fleischmann/Sachs, pl. 58.
Lent by the Museum Boymans-van Beuningen, Rotterdam

The most finished study for the water-colour in the Metropolitan Museum of Art, New York.

156 Two Print Collectors
Deux amateurs d'estampes

Pen and water-colour: 29 by 34 (11⅜ by 13⅜).
Lent by the Museo Nacional de Bellas Artes, Buenos Aires

Unrecorded study for the water-colour of the same title in the Victoria and Albert Museum (Ionides Collection). The tracing in the Gerstenberg Collection may have been made either from the present study or from the finished water-colour.

157 The Picture Sale
La vente de tableaux

Charcoal and wash: 11·5 by 9·5 (4⅝ by 3¾). L.l.c.: *h.D.*
PROVENANCE: M. Liebermann; Riezler.
EXHIBITION: Matthiesen, 1926 (122).
LITERATURE: Fuchs, p. 46, ill. 67; Cat. of a Sale at Berne (Gutekunst & Klipstein), 3 December 1949, No. 34.
Lent by Dr Zdenko Bruck, Buenos Aires

Study for a larger woodcut, *L'expert* (Bouvy 939), which served as an illustration to an article by Champfleury, *L'Hôtel des Commissaires-priseurs*, published in *Monde illustré* in March 1863.

158 The Connoisseur
L'amateur

Pen and wash over black chalk: 13·4 by 11·5 (5⅝ by 4½). L.r.c.: *h.D.*
PROVENANCE: Mrs. J. D. Rockefeller; Mrs Martin; Schaeffer.
LITERATURE: Maison, *Drawings*, ill. 115.
Lent by Mr Gregoire Tarnopol, New York

159 At the Exhibition
A l'exposition de tableaux

Pen and ink, red chalk, charcoal and stump and sepia washes: 15 by 14 (5⅞ by 5½). L.r.c.: *h. Daumier à Madame Jacquette.*
PROVENANCE: Jacquette; Reveillé; Dieterle.
LITERATURE: Maison, *Drawings*, ill. 122.
Lent by Monsieur Roger Delapalme, Paris

160 Death and the Doctors
La Mort et les médecins

Charcoal, lightly washed: 38 by 24 (15 by 9½).
EXHIBITION: Paris, Galerie Sagot-Le Garrec, *Exposition Daumier sculpteur*, 1957 (77).

LITERATURE: Maison, *Drawings*, ill. 99.
Lent by Monsieur A. Strolin, Neuilly-sur-Seine

Study connected with the water-colour in the collection of Dr Oskar Reinhart, Winterthur. The scene illustrates the end of a La Fontaine story: after the patient's death both doctors argue that he would still be alive, had his colleague only heeded his advice.

161 Prison Scene
Scène de prison—Scène de torture

Pen and wash over black chalk: 19 by 26 (7½ by 10¼).

PROVENANCE: Schuffenecker; Ackermann; P. M. Turner; Matthiesen; Wertheimer.

EXHIBITIONS: Beaux-Arts, 1901 (482); Matthiesen, 1926 (135).

LITERATURE: *Drucke der Marées Gesellschaft*, IX, *Daumier*, Munich, 1918, pl. 3; Klossowski, 84 and pl. 62; Fuchs, 240b; Fleischmann/Sachs, pl. 5; R. Huyghe and P. Jacottet, *Le Dessin Français au XIXᵉ siècle*, 1948, pl. 53; Adhémar, *Drawings*, pl. 22.

Lent by Professor A. Hottinger, Basle

A charcoal sketch connected with this stage scene is in the collection of Monsieur Claude Roger-Marx, Paris.

162 The Vigil
La Veille—La veille funèbre

Pen and ink: 23 by 29 (9 by 11⅜).

PROVENANCE: Vollard; Cassirer.

LITERATURE: Maison, *Drawings*, ill. 107.

Lent by Mr Curtis O. Baer, New Rochelle, N.Y.

A somewhat caricatured version of this drawing (reproduced Martine-Marotte, pl. 18) was formerly with Bignou, Paris.

163 Scene from a Comedy by Molière
Recherches de personnages du théatre de Molière

Pen and wash: 13·5 by 16 (5¼ by 6⅜). Inscribed by Arsène Alexandre.

PROVENANCE: Alexandre; Coquelin; Wertheimer; Durand; Reid.

LITERATURE: Maison, *Drawings*, ill. 87.

Lent by Mr and Mrs Philip J. Goldberg, London

164 Characters from a Comedy by Molière
Personnages de Molière—Sganarelle et Monsieur Purgon　　　PLATE 28A

Black chalk and water-colour: 15·6 by 22·9 (6⅛ by 9). L.l.: *h.D.*

PROVENANCE: Darrasse; Strolin; Bernheim Jeune.

EXHIBITION: On loan to the Tate Gallery, 1924 and 1929.

LITERATURE: *Cat. de la Vente Darrasse*, Paris, 1909, No. 73; Klossowski, 68B; Fuchs, 336; Escholier, 1930, pl. 58, and 1938, p. 139; Fleischmann/Sachs, pl. 39; Lassaigne, pl. 142; Gobin, *Daumier Sculpteur*, 1952, p. 290 (detail); Schweicher, pl. 50; Maison, *Drawings*, ill. 96.

Lent by the Corporation of Glasgow, Burrell Collection

Probably drawn about 1845–50. Gobin (op. cit., No. 59) tentatively attributes a bust, modelled in clay, *L'Homme à la Large Perruque*, to Daumier and suggests a possible connection with the character on the right in the present drawing.

165 Le Malade Imaginaire
Le malade—Les médecins　　　PLATE 28B

Black chalk and water-colour: 19·5 by 26·5 (1½ by 10⅜). L.l.c.: *h. Daumier.*

PROVENANCE: Lemaire; Bignou; Reid & Lefevre; S. Courtauld.

EXHIBITIONS: New York, 1930 (98); London, Royal Academy, *French Art, 1200–1900*, 1932 (904); London, Tate Gallery, *Samuel Courtauld Memorial Exhibition*, 1948 (90); Bibliothèque Nationale, 1958 (211).

LITERATURE: *Cahiers d'Art*, III, 1928, p. 194; Fuchs, 337; *Commemorative Cat. of the Exhibition of French Art at the Royal Academy, 1932*, 1933. No 805 and pl. 192; D. Cooper, Cat. of the Courtauld Collection, 1954, No. 113 and pl. 72; *Marseille, Revue Municipale* (Marseilles), No. 29, 1956, p. 39; Maison, *Drawings*, ill. 98.

Lent by the Courtauld Institute of Art, London

166 Study of an Actor
Etude pour un acteur　　　PLATE 28C

Pen and wash: 24 by 16 (9½ by 6⅜).

PROVENANCE: Lousada; Maison; Nathan.

EXHIBITIONS: London, Whitechapel Art Gallery,

French Exhibition, 1932; Geneva, Musée d'Art et d'Histoire, *De Watteau à Cézanne*, 1951 (106).

LITERATURE: F. Daulte, *Le Dessin français de David à Courbet*, 1953, pl. 21; Maison, *Drawings*, ill. 93.

Lent by Mr Emery Reves

167 Study of an Actor with a Tambourine

Acteur au tambourin

Black chalk: 41 by 28 (16⅛ by 11).

PROVENANCE: Vollard; Kaganovich; Nathan; Zinser.

LITERATURE: Maison, *Drawings*, ill. 90.

Lent by Mr and Mrs Richard S. Davis, Wayzata (Minn.)

168 A Theatre Audience   PLATE 28D

Les spectateurs—Foyer de théâtre

Pen and water-colour, heightened with gouache: 34 by 29 (13⅜ by 11⅜). L.l.c.: *h. Daumier.*

PROVENANCE: Private collection, France; de Hauke; Knoedler.

EXHIBITION: New York, Metropolitan Museum, *The Collection of Mr Walter C. Baker*, 1960 (no catalogue).

LITERATURE: *Cat. d'une Vente à la Galerie Charpentier*, Paris, 9 March 1956, No. 8.

Lent by Mr Walter C. Baker, New York

169 Two Spectators

Deux spectateurs   PLATE 28E

Pen and wash: 24·1 by 19 (9½ by 7½). L.l.: *A mon ami Larochenoire h.D.*

PROVENANCE: de Hauke.

EXHIBITION: On loan to the Joslyn Memorial Museum, Omaha (Neb.), 1941.

LITERATURE: Fuchs, 313; Maison, *Drawings*, ill. 14.

Lent by Mr John Nicholas Brown, Providence, R.I.

170 Study of two Spectators

Etude de deux spectateurs

Black chalk, pen and ink: 13·5 by 13·2 (5⅜ by 5¼). (Framed with a charcoal sketch of three heads, 4·2 by 10·5 (1¾ by 4⅛)).

Lent by Monsieur Jacques Dubourg, Paris

171 Study of four Spectators

Quatre spectateurs

Pen and ink over black chalk: 15·3 by 25·7 (6 by 10⅛). L.l.c.: *h. Daumier.*

PROVENANCE: Reid & Lefevre.

EXHIBITION: Paris, Salon, 1865.

LITERATURE: *L'Autographe au Salon de 1865* (No. 11), 8 juillet 1865, p. 88; E. Bouvy, *Daumier: L'œuvre gravé du Maitre*, II, 1933, Nos. 962–64; Maison, *Drawings*, ill. 13.

Lent by Monsieur Marcel Lecomte, Paris

The drawing is very much earlier than 1865, when the *Autographe au Salon*, which had already reproduced several drawings by the artist in 1864, assembled ten facsimiles of his sketches on one of its large pages. The signature of the present drawing, seen on only a very few of Daumier's studies, was used to sign the whole page.

172 Spectators

Spectateurs—Etude de têtes d'Hommes

Pen and ink: 11·6 by 20·8 (4½ by 8¼). L.r.c.: *h.D.* Verso a study of a lawyer.

PROVENANCE: Koenigs.

On the same mount:

Scene from a Tragedy

Scène d'une tragédie

Pen and ink: 13·2 by 20·8 (5¼ by 8¼). L.r.c.: *h.D.*

PROVENANCE: Roger Marx (?); Koenigs.

EXHIBITIONS (both drawings): Rotterdam, Museum Boymans, *Verzameling Koenigs*, 1935–36 (18–19); Albertina, 1936 (22–23).

LITERATURE (both drawings): Maison, *Drawings*, ills. 104 and 94, respectively.

Lent by the Museum Boymans-van Beuningen, Rotterdam

173 Pierrot and Columbine   PLATE 28F

Pen and ink over charcoal: 42 by 29·7 (16½ by 11¾).

PROVENANCE: Cassirer; Koenigs.

EXHIBITIONS: Rotterdam, Museum Boymans, *Van Ingres tot Seurat*, 1933–34 (35); Rotterdam, Museum Boymans, *Verzameling Koenigs*, 1935–36 (12); Albertina, 1936 (5); Zürich, Kunsthaus, *Von David zu Millet*, 1937 (48).

LITERATURE: Huyghe and Jaccottet, *Le Dessin Français au XIXe siècle*, 1948, pl. 50; Maison, *Drawings*, ill. 86.

Lent by the Museum Boymans-van Beuningen, Rotterdam

174 A Dancer

Une danseuse PLATE 27 I

Black chalk over charcoal and stump: 15 by 11 (5⅞ by 4⅜).

PROVENANCE: Aubry; Rosenwald.

EXHIBITION: Galerie Dru, 1927 (42).

LITERATURE: Fuchs, 264a.

Lent by the National Gallery of Art, Washington Rosenwald Collection

Extremely close in style and movement to the *danseuse* in the lithograph Delteil 2907 (plate 11 of the *Croquis dramatiques*), published in 1857.

175 Sheet of Studies: A Contrast

Un contraste—Le gros et le maigre

Pen and ink: 39·6 by 28·3 (15⅝ by 11⅛). Verso studies of characters from a Comedy, in black chalk and pen and ink. L.r.c.: *h.D.*

PROVENANCE: Bureau; Cassirer; Koenigs.

EXHIBITIONS: Beaux-Arts, 1901 (164); Rotterdam, Museum Boymans, *Van Ingres tot Seurat*, 1933–34 (30); Orangerie, 1934 (191); Rotterdam, Museum Boymans, *Verzameling Koenigs*, 1935–36 (5); Albertina, 1936 (47); Zürich, Kunsthaus, *Von David zu Millet*, 1937 (50).

LITERATURE: *Cat. de la Vente P. Bureau*, Paris, 1927, No. 70; Fuchs, 334a; Adhémar, p. 74 (text illustration).

Lent by the Museum Boymans-van Beuningen, Rotterdam

176 The Wrestlers

Les lutteurs

Pencil: 30·7 by 25·8 (12⅛ by 10⅛).

PROVENANCE: Sarlin.

LITERATURE: A. Stix, *Von Ingres bis Cézanne: 32 Handzeichnungen Französischer Meister des XIX. Jahrhunderts* [in the Albertina], Vienna, 1927, pl. 10; Maison, in *Burl. Mag.*, June 1956, p. 200 and Fig. 21.

Lent by the Graphische Sammlung Albertina, Vienna

Study for the picture in the Ordrupgaardsamlingen, Copenhagen (see No. 65). If the painting is as late as Adhémar suggests (1865–68), this drawing must have preceded it by many years.

177 The Athlete

L'athlète PLATE 28H

Pencil: 24·5 by 18·7 (9⅝ by 7⅜). A similar study on verso.

PROVENANCE: Meller.

LITERATURE: Maison, *Drawings*, ill. 78.

Lent by the Graphische Sammlung Albertina, Vienna

178 Mountebank playing the Drum

Saltimbanque jouant du tambour—L'escamoteur—Paillasse PLATE 29C

Pen and water-colour, heightened with gouache: 35·5 by 25·5 (14 by 10). L.r.c.: *h. Daumier.*

PROVENANCE: Berger; Dollfus.

EXHIBITIONS: Paris, Ecole des Beaux-Arts, *Dessins de l'école moderne*, 1884 (116); Beaux-Arts, 1901 (112); Orangerie, 1934 (111).

LITERATURE: *International Studio* (N.Y.), Vol. 45, 1908, p. 149; Klossowski, 213; Fuchs, 329; Maison, *Drawings*, ill. 82.

Lent by Monsieur César M. de Hauke, Paris

This figure of a mountebank appears in a large group of sketches, tracings, wash drawings and water-colours, mostly as the central figure of a *Parade* (see No. 179). They probably date from the mid-1860s. The present water-colour is the most finished one of the group.

179 The Side-show

La parade PLATE 29D

Black chalk, pencil and wash: 40·6 by 29·5 (16 by 11⅝). L.l.c.: *A mon ami Jules Dupré h.D.*

PROVENANCE: J. Dupré; Marcel Dupré; Déperdussin; Jacobi; Simonson; Barbizon House; Burrell.

EXHIBITIONS: Durand-Ruel, 1878 (155); *La Caricature*, 1888 (404); Galerie Dru, 1923 (50); on loan to the Tate Gallery, 1929; London, Royal Academy, *French Art, 1200–1900*, 1932 (922); Arts Council travelling exhibition, *French Paintings of the 19th Century from the Burrell Collection*, 1950 (20).

LITERATURE: Alexandre, p. 377; Escholier, 1923, plate facing p. 18, and 1930, pl. 73; Sadleir, pl. 6; *Ars Graphica*, pl. 42; Martine-Marotte, pl. 5; *Barbizon House: An Illustrated Souvenir for 1924*, pl. 33; Fuchs, 257b; *Commemorative Cat. of the Exhibition of French Art at the Royal Academy, 1932*, 1933. No. 809; Fleischmann/Sachs, pl. 13; Adhémar, *Drawings*, pl. 51 ('1868').

Lent by the Corporation of Glasgow, Burrell Collection

The most finished study for the water-colour in the Esnault-Pelterie Collection. The sequence of the several tracings, line and wash drawings of this subject remains problematic.

180 The Side-show

La parade   PLATE 29A

Pen and ink and black chalk over charcoal and red chalk: 39 by 30·7 (15⅜ by 12⅛). L.r.c.: *h.D.*
PROVENANCE: F. Hatvany.
EXHIBITION: Budapest, Museum of Fine Arts, *French Drawings*, 1933 (cat. p. 325).
LITERATURE: *Magyar Müvészet* [Hungarian Art], Budapest, 1933, p. 325; D. Pataky, *Von Delacroix bis Picasso, Zeichnungen aus der Sammlung des Museums der Bildenden Künste in Budapest*, Budapest, 1958, No. 29 and pl. 29.
Lent by the Museum of Fine Arts, Budapest

Various versions of this subject are known, some in water-colour, others in pen and ink or in black chalk, and they vary in size from the smallest sketches—sometimes of one or two of the main figures only—to drawings on a fairly large scale. In some versions an audience is indicated in the foreground (see No. 181), in others, as the well-known water-colour in the Louvre, the figures are shown not quite full-length. The present drawing is a study for three of the five figures in that water-colour, although on a larger scale.

181 The Side-show

La parade   PLATE 29B

Pen and ink over charcoal and brown chalk, lightly washed: 38·6 by 34·4 (15¼ by 13½).
PROVENANCE: Amélie Geoffroy; Henraux; Valdo-Barbey; P. Rosenberg.
EXHIBITIONS: Durand-Ruel, 1878 (135); Beaux-Arts, 1901 (207); Albertina, 1936 (12).

LITERATURE: C. Roger-Marx, *Daumier*, Paris, 1938, p. 17; Huyghe and Jaccottet, *Le Dessin français au XIXᵉ siècle*, 1948, pl. 51.
Lent from a Private Collection, New York

Probably the only important drawing of this group of *Parade foraine* versions which does not appear to be immediately connected with any other study. See note on No. 180.

182 A Clown and a Drummer

Paillasse et tambour

Pen and wash: 10·5 by 9·5 (4⅛ by 3¾). L.r.c.: *h.D.*
PROVENANCE: Jaquette.
LITERATURE: Maison, *Drawings*, ill. 73.
Lent by Monsieur Jean Dieterle, Paris

Probably the first idea for the drawing in the Metropolitan Museum of Art, New York. See also No. 183.

183 A Clown and a Drummer

Paillasse—La parade

Charcoal and black and brown chalks: 40·6 by 36 (16 by 14⅛).
PROVENANCE: A. D. Geoffroy; Kapferer; Böhler; Cassirer; Keonigs.
EXHIBITIONS: Beaux-Arts, 1901 (206); Rotterdam, Museum Boymans, *Van Ingres tot Seurat*, 1933–34 (26); Basle, Kunsthalle, *Meisterzeichnungen französischer Künstler von Ingres bis Cézanne*, 1935 (78); Rotterdam, Museum Boymans, *Verzameling Koenigs*, 1935–36 (1); Albertina, 1936 (18); Zürich, Kunsthaus, *Von David bis Millet*, 1937 (47).
LITERATURE: Klossowski, 210; *Ars Graphica*, pl. 46; Fuchs, 261b; Scheiwiller, pl. 26; Lassaigne, pl. 142; Maison, *Drawings*, ill. 71.
Lent by the Museum Boymans-van Beuningen, Rotterdam

The most finished of several studies for the drawing in the Metropolitan Museum of Art, New York. See also No. 182.

184 Mountebanks moving out   PLATE 28G

Le déplacement des saltimbanques— Paillasses—Maigre recette

Black chalk and stump, and pen and wash, heightened with sanguine and water-colour: 36·5 by 27·1 (14⅜ by 10⅝). L.l.c.: *h.D.*

PROVENANCE: Amélie Geoffroy (?); F. C. Sumner.

EXHIBITION: Possibly Beaux-Arts, 1901 (205).

LITERATURE: Klossowski, 206 and pl. 89; *Cat. d'une Vente anon.*, Paris, 4 avril 1928, No. 25; *The Arts*, May 1929, p. 296, and May 1930, p. 74; Fleischmann/Sachs, pl. 15; Lassaigne, pl. 150; Escholier, 1938, p. 51; Maison, in *Burl. Mag.* January 1954, pp. 16–17 and Fig. 18; Adhémar, *Drawings*, pl. 49 ('1867'); Adhémar, pl. 158 ('*vers* 1866'); Maison, *Drawings*, ill. 77.

Lent by the Wadsworth Atheneum, Hartford, Conn.

Engraved by P. S. F. Teyssonnières. Two preparatory drawings, one of them based on a reversed tracing of the first study, are in private collections in Paris (Maison, *Drawings*, ill. 75–76). Since entering the collection of the Wadsworth Atheneum, this drawing has become one of the most frequently exhibited works in Daumier's œuvre.

185 The Mountebanks

Les Saltimbanques

Pen and ink over charcoal: 31·5 by 35 (12⅜ by 13⅞).

PROVENANCE: Vollard; P. Rosenberg; Camentron; Peutier; Goriany.

EXHIBITIONS: Galerie Rosenberg, 1907 (26); on loan to the Brooklyn Museum, before 1940; Bibliothèque Nationale, 1958 (203).

LITERATURE: Klossowski, 195 and pl. 90; Lassaigne, pl. 152; Maison, in *Burl. Mag.*, May 1956, p. 165 and Fig. 48.

Lent by Monsieur Maurice Loncle, Paris

A study, partly traced and in reverse, of the central group of the water-colour now in the Victoria and Albert Museum (Ionides Bequest).

186 Waiting at the Station

L'attente à la gare

Pen and ink, charcoal and stump: 24 by 27 (9½ by 10⅝). L.r.c.: *h.D.*

PROVENANCE: Davis; P. M. Turner; Durand-Matthiesen; Dr J. Hohl.

LITERATURE: *International Studio* (N.Y.), Vol. XIV, 1915, p. 7; Klossowski, 250A; A. Bertram, *Honoré Daumier* ('World's Masters' series), 1929, pl. XVI; *Journal of the Walters Art Gallery*, III, Baltimore, 1940, p. 40 and Fig. 33; Cat. of the Sir Edmund Davis Sale, London, 1942, No. 40 (as 'A Peasant Family seated').

Lent by Dr Johannes R. Hohl, Toms River, N.J.

Study for the water-colour in the Victoria and Albert Museum (Ionides Collection).

187 The Departure of the Train

Le départ du train—Le départ pour le chemin de fer—La gare Saint-Lazare

PLATE 26C

Black chalk, pen and water-colour: 14·5 by 25 (5¾ by 9⅞). U.r.c.: *h. Daumier.*

PROVENANCE: H. Rouart; Brame; Beurdeley; Reid & Lefevre; Knoedler; Duncan Phillips; Kraushaar; Ralph T. King; Charles King.

EXHIBITIONS: Paris, Ecole des Beaux-Arts, *Dessins de l'école moderne*, 1884 (117); *La Caricature*, 1888 (379); Paris, *Exposition Centennale*, 1889 (138); Paris, Galerie Brunner, *Exposition des Peintres et Graveurs*, 1913 (160); Geneva, Musée d'Art et d'Histoire, *L'école française du XIXᵉ siècle*, 1918 (152); on loan to the Cleveland Museum of Art, 1952.

LITERATURE: Alexandre, p. 377; *Cat. de la Vente H. Rouart*, Paris, 1912, II, No. 32; *Cat. de la Vente A. Beurdeley*, Paris, 1920, V, No. 100; Klossowski, 249; Sadleir, pl. 20; *Ars Graphica*, pl. 7; Fuchs, 223a.

Lent by Mrs Gilbert P. Schaefer, Cleveland, Ohio

Probably drawn about 1862.

188 The First-class Carriage   PLATE 26E

Intérieur d'un wagon de première classe

Black chalk and water-colour, heightened with gouache: 20·5 by 30 (8⅛ by 11¾). L.l.c.: *h. Daumier.*

PROVENANCE: Lucas; W. T. Walters; H. Walters.

LITERATURE: A. Mongan, in *Gazette des Beaux-Arts*, 1937, pp. 251–3 and Fig. 4; id., in *Art News* (N.Y.), 14 August 1937, p. 12; id., in *Art Digest* (N.Y.), 1 October 1937, p. 6; S. L. Faison, *The Third Class Railway Carriage in the Metropolitan Museum of Art, New York* (Gallery Books, 13), n.d. (1946), pl. 2; Maison, *Drawings*, ill. 50.

Lent by the Walters Art Gallery, Baltimore

Bought by M. Lucas, for Walters, from Daumier in 1864. A roughly drawn charcoal study for this composition is in the E. Whye Collection, New York.

189 The Second-class Carriage

Intérieur d'un wagon de deuxième classe
    PLATE 26D

Black chalk and water-colour: 20·5 by 30·1 (8¼ by 11⅞). L.l.c.: *h. Daumier.*

PROVENANCE: Lucas; W. T. Walters; H. Walters.

LITERATURE: A. Mongan, in *Gazette des Beaux-Arts*, 1937, pp. 251–3 and Fig. 5; id., in *Art News* (N.Y.), 14 August 1937, p. 12; id., in *Art Digest* (N.Y.), 1 October 1937, p. 6; C. Roger-Marx, *Daumier*, Paris, 1938, p. 47; S. L. Faison, *The Third Class Railway Carriage in the Metropolitan Museum of Art, New York* (Gallery Books, 13) n.d. (1946), pl. 3; Adhémar, *Drawings*, pl. 30 ('1864').

Lent by the Walters Art Gallery, Baltimore

Bought by M. Lucas, for Walters, from Daumier. According to Adhémar, this purchase was made on 13 April 1864 when the artist delivered the finished drawing to the American who commissioned it. On the other hand, a woodcut by C. Maurand, after this or a practically identical drawing, had already been published as early as 18 January 1862 in *Monde illustré* (see E. Bouvy, *Daumier: L'œuvre gravé du Maître*, II, 1933, No. 921). There is also a painted version of this composition as well as several imitations in oil and water-colour.

190 The Third-class Carriage   PLATE 26F

Intérieur d'un wagon de troisième classe
Black chalk and water-colour, heightened with gouache: 20·3 by 29·5 (8 by 11⅝). L.r.c.: *h. Daumier.*

PROVENANCE: Lucas; W. T. Walters; H. Walters.

EXHIBITION: Galerie Rosenberg, 1907 (8).

LITERATURE: A. Mongan, in *Gazette des Beaux-Arts*, 1937, pp. 251–3, and Fig. 6; id., in *Art News* (N.Y.), 14 August 1937, p. 12; id., in *Art Digest* (N.Y.), 1 October 1937, p. 6; H. Marceau and D. Rosen, in *Journal of the Walters Art Gallery*, III, Baltimore, 1940, pp. 9 ff.; S. L. Faison, *The Third Class Railway Carriage in the Metropolitan Museum of Art, New York* (Gallery Books, 13), n.d. (1946), p. 4; Shoolman and Slatkin, *Six Centuries of French Master Drawings in America*, N.Y., 1950, pl. 85; Adhémar, *Drawings*, pl. 31 ('1864').

Lent by the Walters Art Gallery, Baltimore

Miss A. Mongan's assumption that this drawing preceded the painted versions is probably correct. Daumier very possibly used a squared tracing of it for transfer to canvas (see No. 69).

191 A Third-class Carriage

Un wagon de troisième classe   PLATE 26B
Pen and ink over charcoal, partly washed with water-colour: 22 by 31 (8⅝ by 12¼).

PROVENANCE: G. Mathias; S. Posen; Mohrenwitz.

EXHIBITIONS: Paris, *Exposition Centennale*, 1900 (852); Beaux-Arts, 1901 (227).

LITERATURE: Klossowski, 256; Maison, *Drawings*, ill. 49; *Katalog Nachlass Dr L. Mohrenwitz*, Lucerne, 1960, No. 480.

Lent by Herr Max Wydler, Zürich

A study for the very finished water-colour in the collection of Dr Oskar Reinhart, Winterthur. Among the many variations on the *Wagon de troisième classe* theme only these two variants of this particular composition are known.

192 The Omnibus

Intérieur d'un Omnibus—Wagon de troisième classe   PLATE 26A
Charcoal, pencil, pen and ink, wash and water-colour: 23·5 by 33·4 (9¼ by 13¼).

PROVENANCE: Lemaire; Mlle Geoffroy.

EXHIBITIONS: Durand-Ruel, 1878 (125); Beaux-Arts, 1901 (204); Albertina, 1936 (39).

LITERATURE: Klossowski, 260; Martine-Marotte, pl. 8; Maison, *Drawings*, ill. 45.

Lent by Monsieur A. Strolin, Neuilly-sur-Seine

193 The Omnibus

L'omnibus

Black chalk and water-colour: sight size, 11·5 by 22·7 (4½ by 9). L.l.c.: *h. Daumier.*

PROVENANCE: Hugh Lane.

LITERATURE: Klossowski, 260A; Fuchs, 225a; Maison, *Drawings*, ill. 44.

Lent by the Municipal Gallery of Modern Art, Dublin

194 Henri Monnier as 'Joseph Prudhomme'

Henri Monnier dans le rôle de Prudhomme—Portrait de Monnier   PLATE 27H
Black chalk, pen and wash: 41·5 by 29·5 (16⅜ by 11⅝). Verso a black chalk study for a Barker in a Side-show.

PROVENANCE: Gobin; Cassirer; Koenigs.

EXHIBITIONS: Rotterdam, Museum Boymans, *Van Ingres tot Seurat*, 1933–34 (27); Basle, Kunsthalle, *Meisterzeichnungen französischer Künstler von Ingres bis Cézanne*, 1935 (79); Rotterdam, Museum Boymans, *Verzameling Koenigs*, 1935–36 (2); Albertina, 1936 (46); Zürich, Kunsthaus, *Von David zu Millet*, 1937 (49).

LITERATURE: Fuchs 180; Gobin, *Daumier Sculpteur*, 1952, p. 315; Adhémar, *Drawings*, 1954, pl. 28 (*'vers 1857'*); Maison, *Drawings*, ill. 91.

Lent by the Museum Boymans-van Beuningen, Rotterdam

Henri Monnier (1799–1877), a friend of Daumier, was a writer and a draughtsman of no mean ability. Joseph Prudhomme was a character of his creation, widely known and popular at the time. Adhémar suggests that the present drawing may have been intended as a frontispiece for Monnier's *Mémoires de Joseph Prudhomme*, which appeared in 1857.

195 The Butcher

Le boucher—Le charcutier   PLATE 25D

Pen and black chalk with wash and water-colour, heightened with white gouache: 27 by 20 (10⅝ by 7⅞). L.l.c.: *h.D.*

PROVENANCE: Bureau; P. Rosenberg.

EXHIBITIONS: Durand-Ruel, 1878 (111); Beaux-Arts, 1901 (129).

LITERATURE: Alexandre, p. 377; Klossowski, 242; *Cat. de la Vente P. Bureau*, Paris, 1927, No. 76; Fuchs, 324; Escholier, 1930, pl. 79; Fleischmann/Sachs, pl. 37; Lassaigne, pl. 100; Mongan and Sachs, *Drawings in the Fogg Museum of Art*, Cambridge (Mass.), 1940, I, No. 656 and III, Fig. 332; Adhémar, *Drawings*, pl. 25; Adhémar, pl. 95 (*'vers 1856/60'*); Schweicher, pl. 42; Kalitina, pl. 62; Ziller, pl. 92.

Lent by the Fogg Art Museum, Harvard University, Cambridge, Mass.

A very similar water-colour is in the Gerstenberg Collection.

196 The Butcher

Le boucher—Le charcutier

Black chalk over charcoal and stump: 33·2 by 23·2 (11⅞ by 9⅛).

PROVENANCE: Henraux.

EXHIBITIONS: Galerie Dru, 1927 (43); Orangerie, 1934 (79); Albertina, 1936 (9).

Lent by Monsieur Jacques Dubourg, Paris

197 Study of a Lawyer

L'avocat   PLATE 34B

Black chalk, pen and wash: 20·7 by 13·9 (8⅛ by 5½). L.r.c.: *h.D.*

PROVENANCE: Bureau; Cassirer; Koenigs.

EXHIBITIONS: Durand-Ruel, 1878 (120); Beaux-Arts, 1901 (137); Rotterdam, Museum Boymans, *Van Ingres tot Seurat*, 1933–34 (32); Orangerie, 1934 (132a); Basle, Kunsthalle, *Meisterzeichnungen französischer Künstler von Ingres bis Cézanne*, 1935 (84); Rotterdam, Museum Boymans, *Verzameling Koenigs*, 1935–36 (9); Albertina, 1936 (35); Zürich, Kunsthaus, *Von David zu Millet*, 1937 (55).

LITERATURE: Alexandre, p. 378; Klossowski, 144; *Cat. de la Vente P. Bureau*, Paris, 1927, No. 62; Fuchs, 194b; Huyghe and Jaccottet, *Le Dessin français au XIXe siècle*, 1948, pl. 55; Fleischmann/Sachs, pl. 23; Adhémar, *Drawings*, pl. 1; Adhémar, pl. 150 (*'vers 1865'*).

Lent by the Museum Boymans-van Beuningen, Rotterdam

198 Lawyer with his Client

Avocat et client—Défenseur et accusé

Black chalk and wash: 15 by 15·7 (5⅞ by 6⅛). L.l.c.: *h.D.*

PROVENANCE: A. Rouart; H. Rouart; Guiot; Matthiesen; Wertheimer.

EXHIBITIONS: Beaux-Arts, 1901 (258); *Daumier-Gavarni*, 1923 (62); Galerie Dru, 1927 (28); Orangerie, 1934 (137); Copenhagen, Statens Museum, *Franske Haandtegninger*, 1939 (20).

LITERATURE: Escholier, 1923, p. 128; Martine-Marotte, pl. 26; Fuchs, 196b.

Lent by Dr Max Schmidheiny, Heerbrugg (Switzerland)

199 Lawyer with a Woman Client

Avocat et sa cliente   PLATE 34F

Pen and water-colour: 16·5 by 21·5 (6½ by 8½).

PROVENANCE: Castagnary; Durand-Ruel; P. Rosenberg; Gwendoline E. Davies.

EXHIBITION: *La Caricature*, 1888 (396).

LITERATURE: Klossowski, 113D; Sadleir, pl. 39; *Ars Graphica*, pl. 17; Fuchs, 195c; Lassaigne, pl. 82; Schweicher, pl. 26.
Lent by the National Museum of Wales, Cardiff

200 The Conceited Lawyer PLATE 34A

L'avocat suffisant—Avocat et cliente

Pen, black chalk and water-colour: 28 by 21 (11 by 8¼). L.l.c.: *h.D.*

PROVENANCE: G. Bernheim; Gobin.

EXHIBITIONS: Leicester Galleries, 1936 (81); Pittsburgh, Carnegie Institute, *A Hundred Prints and Drawings from the Collection of H. Lockhart, Jr.*, 1939, p. 145 of cat. .

LITERATURE: *Ars Graphica*, pl. 23; Fuchs 205b; Scheiwiller, pl. XIX; Lassaigne, pl. 80; Schweicher, pl. 28.

Lent by Mr James H. Lockhart, Jr., Geneseo, N.Y.

201 Before the Hearing: A Lawyer with his Client PLATE 30C

Avant l'audience: avocat et client

Black chalk, pen and water-colour: 16·8 by 21·5 (6⅝ by 8½). L.r.c.: *h. Daumier.*

PROVENANCE: Bernheim Jeune.

EXHIBITION: Buenos Aires, Museo Nacional de Bellas Artes, *Dibujos siglos XIX y XX*, 1959 (17).

LITERATURE: *The Magazine of Art* (Washington), February 1942, p. 56.

Lent by Señor Antonio Santamarina, Buenos Aires

202 The Stairway of the Palais de Justice PLATE 30A

Le grand escalier du Palais de Justice

Pen over black chalk, washed with water-colour and gouache: 36 by 26·6 (14⅛ by 10½). L.l.c.: *h. Daumier.*

PROVENANCE: Lucas; on loan to Baltimore Museum of Art since 1934.

EXHIBITIONS: Paris, Ecole des Beaux-Arts, *Dessins de l'école moderne*, 1884 (119); Galerie Rosenberg, 1907 (9).

LITERATURE: Klossowski, 127; Fuchs, 183 (wood-cut reproduction).

Lent by the Maryland Institute, Baltimore, Lucas

Collection, by courtesy of the Baltimore Museum of Art

Probably bought by M. Lucas from the artist on the occasion of one of his visits to Daumier's studio, in 1864. The painting in the Boston Museum of Fine Arts, which treats a similar subject, is very much earlier, while a drawing reproduced by Fuchs (op. cit., 202b) is certainly a study for the central figure in this composition.

203 Two Lawyers

Deux avocats PLATE 31A

Black chalk and water-colour: 22 by 16·2 (8⅝ by 6⅜). L.l.c.: *h. Daumier.*

PROVENANCE: Verdier(?); Vasnier.

EXHIBITIONS: Possibly Durand-Ruel, 1878 (213); Beaux-Arts, 1901 (287).

LITERATURE: *Catalogue Sommaire de la Collection Henry Vasnier*, Rheims, 1913; C. Rim, *Au Temps de Daumier*, 1935, plate facing p. 85; Maison, *Drawings*, ill. 130.

Lent by the Musée des Beaux-Arts, Rheims

Probably drawn about 1850–55.

204 Two Lawyers

Deux avocats

White chalk on tinted paper, laid down on board: 26·5 by 21·5 (10½ by 8½).

PROVENANCE: Régereau; Vollard; Dubourg.

EXHIBITION: Beaux-Arts, 1901 (257).

LITERATURE: Klossowski, 162; *Cat. d'une Vente anon.*, Paris, 28 May 1952, No. 11; *Cat. d'une Vente anon.*, Geneva (Galerie Motte), 15 Oct. 1960, No. 180.

Lent by Roland, Browse and Delbanco, London

Daumier's only known drawing done in this technique, and probably his only drawing on tinted paper. The central figure was used in a painting, the other details of which are not by Daumier.

205 Two Lawyers in Conversation

Deux avocats en conversation—Deux avocats causant—Scène du Palais de Justice—Les avocats PLATE 34C

Black chalk, pen and water-colour: 25·5 by 16·5 (10 by 6½). L.l.c.: *h. Daumier.*

PROVENANCE: Beurdeley; Gobin; Paul J. Sachs.

EXHIBITIONS: Paris, Galerie Brunner, *Exposition des Peintres et Graveurs de Paris*, 1913 (159); Geneva, Musée d'Art et d'Histoire, *L'école française du XIXe siècle*, 1918 (47).

LITERATURE: *Cat. de la Vente Beurdeley*, Paris, 1920, V, No. 101; Klossowski, 165B; *Ars Graphica*, pl. XXI; Fuchs, 207a; Mongan and Sachs, *Drawings in the Fogg Museum of Art*, Cambridge (Mass.), 1940, I, No. 657 and III, pl. 333; *Art Digest* (N.Y.), 15 November 1945, p. 27.

Lent by the Fogg Art Museum, Harvard University, Cambridge, Mass., Meta and Paul Sachs Collection

206 Two Lawyers in Conversation

Deux avocats en conversation   PLATE 31D

Black chalk, stump and wash: 32·2 by 26·5 (12¾ by 10½). L.r.c.: *h.D.*

PROVENANCE: Bureau; Perls; Hofer.

EXHIBITIONS: Durand-Ruel, 1878 (116); *La Caricature*, 1888 (407); Beaux-Arts, 1901 (134).

LITERATURE: Alexandre, p. 378; Klossowski, 142; Fuchs, 142b (after a woodcut reproduction); Escholier, 1930, pl. 85; H. Tietze, *European Master Drawings in the United States*, N.Y., 1947, pl. 137.

Lent by the National Gallery of Art, Washington, gift of Myron A. Hofer in memory of his mother, Jane Arms Hofer

207 Two Lawyers: The Handshake

Deux avocats: La poignée de main

PLATE 30B

Black chalk, pen and water-colour: 13 by 19 (5⅛ by 7½). U.r.: *h. Daumier*.

PROVENANCE: Reich.

LITERATURE: C. G. Heise, *Grosse Zeichner des XIX. Jahrhunderts*, 1959, p. 138, and Fig. 111.

Lent by the Rijksmuseum, Amsterdam (on loan to the Stedelijk Museum)

Drawn about 1855.

208 The two Colleagues

Les deux confrères—Avocats   PLATE 31B

Pen, black chalk and water-colour: 25·3 by 19·1 (10 by 7½). L.l.c.: *h. Daumier*.

PROVENANCE: Geoffroy-Dechaume; Feydeau; Cognacq.

EXHIBITIONS: Durand-Ruel, 1878 (169); *La Caricature*, 1888 (384); Beaux-Arts, 1901 (169); Orangerie, 1934 (142).

LITERATURE: *Cat. de la Vente Geoffroy-Dechaume*, Paris, 1893, No. 55; *Cat. de la Vente Ggs. Feydeau*, Paris, 1901, No. 116; Klossowski, 151; *Cat. de la Vente G. Cognacq*, Paris, 1952, No. 20.

Lent by Mr Edwin C. Vogel, New York

Drawn about 1850–55.

209 Good Colleagues

Bons Confrères

Pen and wash: 26 by 33·6 (10¼ by 13¼). L.l.c.: *h. Daumier*.

EXHIBITIONS: On loan to the Tate Gallery, 1924 and 1929; Arts Council travelling exhibition, *French Paintings of the 19th Century from the Burrell Collection*, 1950 (25).

LITERATURE: D. Talbot Rice, in *Scottish Art Review* (Glasgow), 3, 1946, p. 4.

Lent by the Corporation of Glasgow, Burrell Collection

Dates from about 1860–62. Almost the same subject as the drawing now at Melbourne (see No. 210), but in reverse.

210 My dear Colleague . . .

Mon cher confrère . . .   PLATE 31C

Black chalk and pen and wash, with water-colour and gouache: 28 by 21·8 (11 by 8⅝). L.l.c.: *h. Daumier*.

PROVENANCE: Barbizon House.

LITERATURE: Sadleir, pl. 44; Fuchs, 206b; Lassaigne, pl. 77; Cassou, pl. 14; Maison, in *Burl. Mag.*, March 1954, Fig. 25.

Lent by the National Gallery of Victoria, Melbourne

Drawn about 1860.

211 Members of the Bar   PLATE 32B

Les avocats—Le parquet des avocats

Pen and water-colour, heightened with white gouache: 23 by 31 (9 by 12¼). U.l.: *h. Daumier*.

PROVENANCE: Barbazanges (?); Brame; Knoedler.

EXHIBITIONS: Cambridge (Mass.), Fogg Art Museum, *French Painting of the 19th and 20th Centuries*, 1929 (13); New York, 1930 (103);

Orangerie, 1934 (144); Philadelphia, 1937 (42); on loan to the Joslyn Memorial Museum, Omaha (Neb.), 1941.

LITERATURE: Fuchs, 317; Lassaigne, pl. 85.

Lent by Mr John Nicholas Brown, Providence, R.I.

One of the most elaborately finished water-colours of this subject, probably dating from the early 1860s.

212 Members of the Bar

Les avocats—Avocats et juges, avant l'audience

Pen and water-colour: 16 by 21·6 (6⅜ by 8½). U.l.: *h. Daumier*.

PROVENANCE: Tavernier; Tempelaere; Knoedler.

EXHIBITION: Beaux-Arts, 1901 (282).

LITERATURE: *Cat. de la Vente A. Tavernier*, Paris, 1900, No. 107, and 1907, No. 65; Klossowski, 118 and pl. 78; Fuchs, 190a; Maison, *Drawings*, ill. 133.

Lent by Mrs Charles R. Henschel, New York

Drawn about 1855–58. Two imitations of this composition are known, one of them a water-colour of approximately the same size.

213 Court Room Scene

Scène de Tribunal—Le Plaidoyer

Black chalk and wash, heightened with gouache: 17 by 23 (6¾ by 9). L.l.c.: *h. Daumier*.

PROVENANCE: Forbes; Kuthe; Caspari.

LITERATURE: *Kat. der Sammlung J. S. Forbes*, Munich, 1906, No. 30; *Kat. der Sammlung Kuthe*, Berlin, 1911, No. 13; Klossowski, 171; Fuchs, 184b.

Lent by Mr Bernard S. Kramarsky, Miami, Fla.

Verso a sketch of two lawyers which is not by Daumier.

214 Exhibits for the Prosecution

Les pièces de conviction   PLATE 32A

Black and coloured chalks, pen and wash and water-colour, heightened with white gouache: 31·7 by 46·3 (12½ by 18¼). L.l.c.: *h. Daumier*.

PROVENANCE: Bellino; Lawrence; Sadler; Barbizon House.

EXHIBITIONS: Paris, Louvre, *Exposition de tableaux, statues et objets d'art au profit de l'œuvre des orphelins de l'Alsace Lorraine*, 1885 (102); *La Caricature*, 1888 (393); Paris, *Exposition Centennale*, 1889 (134).

LITERATURE: *Cat. de la Vente A. Bellino*, Paris, 1892, No. 31; Cat. of the Cyrus J. Lawrence Sale, New York, 1910, No. 32; *Art Journal*, 1911, pp. 313 and 323; Klossowski, 134B; Sadleir, pl. 37; Escholier, 1923, p. 159, 1930, pl. 81, and 1938, p. 75; Fuchs, 192b; Fleischmann/Sachs, pl. 29; Lassaigne, pl. 86; Schweicher, pl. 31; Kalitina, pl. 55.

Lent by the National Gallery of Victoria, Melbourne

An unfinished version in water-colour, of the same dimensions, is in the Conrad Bareiss Collection, Zürich.

215 Three Judges at a Hearing

Trois juges en séance—A l'audience

Pen and wash: 13 by 24·5 (5⅝ by 9⅝).

PROVENANCE: H. Rouart; Wallis; Scott.

EXHIBITION: La Caricature, 1888 (380).

LITERATURE: *Cat. de la Vente H. Rouart*, Paris, 1912, II, No. 43; Klossowski, 134; Fuchs, 188a.

Lent by the National Gallery of Canada, Ottawa

A water-colour of the same subject is in the Gerstenberg Collection.

216 A Lawyer reading a Document to the Tribunal

Avocat devant le Tribunal   PLATE 34G

Black chalk and wash: approx. 28 by 38 (11 by 15). L.l.c.: *h.D.*

PROVENANCE: Wertheimer.

LITERATURE: Maison, *Drawings*, ill. 140.

Lent from a Private Collection, Basle

Study for the smaller and carefully finished water-colour in the collection of Dr Oskar Reinhart, Winterthur.

217 Behind closed Doors

Huis clos—Déposition de mineure—Le flagrant délit

Pen and ink: 20·5 by 33·2 (8⅛ by 13⅛).

PROVENANCE: Joyant.

EXHIBITION: Bibliothèque Nationale, 1958 (182).

LITERATURE: Maison, in *Burl. Mag.*, January 1954, p. 14 and Fig. 12; Maison, *Drawings*, ill. 136.

Lent by Monsieur Maurice Loncle, Paris

First study for the wash drawing in the Ny Carlsberg Glyptotek, Copenhagen. A further study is in the Museum Boymans-van Beuningen, Rotterdam.

218 Court Room Scene

Scène de tribunal—Le verdict PLATE 34E

Pen and ink: 35 by 42 ($13\frac{3}{4}$ by $16\frac{1}{2}$).

PROVENANCE: Alexandre; Durand-Ruel; Rosenwald.

EXHIBITION: Philadelphia, Free Library, *Lithographs and drawings by Honoré Daumier lent by Lessing J. Rosenwald*, 1930 (195).

LITERATURE: *Cat. de la Vente Arsène Alexandre*, Paris, 1903, No. 125; Klossowski, 132 and pl. 80; *Ars Graphica*, pl. 13; Fuchs, 201; Shoolman and Slatkin, *Six Centuries of French Master Drawings in America*, N.Y., 1950, pl. 88.

Lent by the National Gallery of Art, Washington, Rosenwald Collection

Probably sketches for a water-colour or painting which, however, is not known to have been executed. Two further very small black chalk sketches for the same composition are in the Claude Roger-Marx Collection, Paris.

219 Court Room Scene PLATE 34D

Avocats—Etude de deux avocats

Pen and wash: 24·5 by 39·5 ($9\frac{5}{8}$ by $15\frac{5}{8}$).

PROVENANCE: D.L. .(?).

LITERATURE: *Kunstwanderer*, 1925, p. 66; Cat. of a Sale at Amsler & Ruthart's, Berlin, 29 October 1925, No. 200; Maison, *Drawings*, ill. 138.

Lent by Monsieur A. Strolin, Neuilly-sur-Seine

Probably the first sketch for the water-colour *Une cause célèbre* in the Esnault-Pelterie Collection. Although the original composition was retained in the water-colour, pen and ink sketches (Maurice Gobin Collection, Paris) of the two lawyers in their final attitudes preceded it.

220 Counsel for the Defence

La défense—Avocat plaidant

Pen and ink, lightly washed: 22·5 by 30 ($8\frac{7}{8}$ by $11\frac{3}{4}$). L.r.c.: *h.D.*

PROVENANCE: G. Lecomte; P. M. Turner; S. Courtauld.

EXHIBITIONS: Beaux-Arts, 1901 (217); *Daumier-Gavarni*, 1923 (80); London, Royal Academy, *French Art, 1200–1900*, 1932 (949); London, Tate Gallery, *Samuel Courtauld Memorial Exhibition*, 1948 (89).

LITERATURE: Klossowski, 152; Martine-Marotte, pl. 31; Fuchs, 184a; *Commemorative Cat. of the Exhibition of French Art at the Royal Academy, 1932*, 1933, No. 814.

Lent by the Courtauld Institute of Art, London

An almost identical second version (23 by 29 cm., unsigned) is in the Gerstenberg Collection. The confusion about the history of the present drawing has arisen because it is described in the earlier literature as measuring 18 by 27 cm.; this was the sight size of the original mount which was discarded when the drawing was cleaned, re-mounted and re-framed.

221 Counsel for the Defence PLATE 33A

Le défenseur—L'avocat lyrique

Black chalk, pen and sepia wash: 23 by 35·9 (9 by 14). L.l.c.: *h.D.*

PROVENANCE: A. Rouart; H. Rouart; de Hauke.

EXHIBITIONS: Beaux-Arts, 1901 (267); *Daumier-Gavarni*, 1923 (83); Galerie Dru, 1927 (27); Orangerie, 1934 (132).

LITERATURE: Escholier, 1923, plate facing p. 108, in colour; *Ars Graphica*, pl. 24; Martine-Marotte, pl. 24; Fuchs, 196c; Fleischmann/Sachs, pl. 26.

Lent by the Phillips Collection, Washington

This composition was repeatedly varied by the artist, in small sketches as well as in very finished water-colours.

222 Counsel for the Defence

Le défenseur—Avocat plaidant—Plaidoirie PLATE 33B

Pen and water-colour over black chalk: 20·2 by 29·2 (8 by $11\frac{1}{2}$). L.l.c.: *h. Daumier.*

PROVENANCE: Heilbuth; Vever; Gallimard; Cassirer; Clark.

EXHIBITIONS: *La Caricature*, 1888 (415); Paris, *Exposition Centennale*, 1889 (136); Galerie Rosenberg, 1907 (15).

LITERATURE: *Cat. de la Vente Heilbuth*, Paris, 1890, No. 327; *Cat. de la Vente H. Vever*, Paris,

1897, No. 137; Klossowski, 129 and pl. 68; Fuchs, note on 186b; Maison, in *Burl. Mag.*, May 1956, p. 165 and Fig. 44.

Lent by the Corcoran Gallery of Art, Washington, W. A. Clark Collection

Another version, identical in every respect except the colouring, is in a private collection in Paris. The tracing used for the transfer from one version to the other came to the Museum Boymans-van Beuningen from the Koenigs collection.

223 Pleading Lawyer

Avocat plaidant—Le plaidoyer

Pen and water-colour: 16 by 22 (6⅜ by 8⅝). L.l.c.: *h. Daumier.*

PROVENANCE: Bellino; H.P. . .; Gallimard; Cassirer; J. Goldschmidt.

EXHIBITIONS: Paris, Louvre, *Exposition de tableaux, statues et objets d'art au profit de l'œuvre des orphelins de l'Alsace Lorraine*, 1885 (101); *La Caricature*, 1888 (392); Paris, *Exposition Centennale*, 1889 (135).

LITERATURE: *Cat. de la Vente Bellino*, Paris, 1892, No. 32; *Cat. de la Vente H.P...*, Paris, 1901, No. 5; Klossowski, 177B; Fuchs, 198a; Maison, *Drawings*, ill. 134.

Lent by Mr and Mrs A. E. Goldschmidt, Stamford, Conn.

A closely related pen and wash study is in the collection of Monsieur Roger Leybold, Paris, while a version in oil on panel (of the central detail only) is a later imitation.

224 Pleading Lawyer

Un avocat plaidant—La plaidoirie

Pen and ink and water-colour over charcoal. 20·4 by 22·7 (8 by 9). L.l.c.: *h.D.* Verso a study of a woman and child, in the same medium.

PROVENANCE: Bureau; Cassirer; Koenigs.

EXHIBITIONS: Durand-Ruel, 1878 (139); Beaux-Arts, 1901 (141); Rotterdam, Museum Boymans, *Van Ingres tot Seurat*, 1933–34 (29); Orangerie, 1934 (33); Rotterdam, Museum Boymans, *Verzameling Koenigs*, 1935–36 (4); Albertina, 1936 (21); Paris, Palais National des Arts, *Chefs d'œuvre de l'Art français*, 1937 (626).

LITERATURE: Alexandre, p. 378; Klossowski, 145; *Cat. de la Vente P. Bureau*, Paris, 1945, No. 52;

Escholier, 1930, pl. 83, and 1938, p. 165; Fuchs, 185a; Fleischmann/Sachs, pl. 24; Adhémar, pl. 22 ('1843/46'); Maison, in *Burl. Mag.*, May 1956, p. 165 and Fig. 45.

Lent by the Museum Boymans-van Beuningen, Rotterdam

A tracing, with the addition of several figures, is in the same Museum; it was used as a basis for the final wash drawing (24 by 34·3 cm.) formerly in the Ryerson Collection, Chicago.

225 Pleading Lawyer

Avocat plaidant—Etude pour un défenseur—Le geste oratoire

Pen and wash: 26·5 by 18·7 (10½ by 7⅜). Verso a similar sketch in pen and ink.

PROVENANCE: Joyant.

EXHIBITION: Bibliothèque Nationale, 1958 (230).

LITERATURE: Maison, *Drawings*, ill. 128.

Lent by Monsieur Maurice Loncle, Paris

226 Pleading Lawyer

Avocat plaidant

Pen and ink: 23 by 16 (9 by 6½). Verso a charcoal study of two figures.

Lent by Monsieur Robert Lebel, Paris

227 Don Quixote and Sancho Panza

PLATE 35C

Charcoal and white chalk on buff paper: 28 by 41 (11 by 16⅛). Verso a charcoal study for a Drunken Silenus.

PROVENANCE: Doria; P. Rosenberg; Gallimard; Cassirer; J. Goldschmidt.

EXHIBITIONS: Beaux-Arts, 1901 (210); Galerie Rosenberg, 1907 (21); Stockholm, Nationalmuseum, *French Art*, 1912 (315).

LITERATURE: *Cat. de la Vente Comte A. Doria*, Paris, 1899, No. 372; Klossowski, 53 and pl. 46; Fuchs, 343b; *Cicerone* (Leipzig), XXII, 1930, p. 9; *Kat. der Sammlung J. G*[oldschmidt]*.*, Berlin, 1941, No. 37.

Lent by Mr A. E. Goldschmidt as executor of his father, the late Mr Jakob Goldschmidt

Study for the grisaille painting in the A. van Beuren Collection (see No. 92).

228 Don Quixote and Sancho Panza

PLATE 35A

Black chalk and water-colour: 13·3 by 19·5 (5¼ by 7⅝). L.l.c.: *h. Daumier*.

PROVENANCE: Jamot.

EXHIBITIONS: Galerie Dru, 1927 (30); Copenhagen, Ny Carlsberg Glyptothek, *Fransk Malerkunst*, 1928 (126); Orangerie, 1934 (119); Basle, Kunsthalle, *Meisterzeichnungen französischer Künstler von Ingres bis Cézanne*, 1935 (91); Grenoble, Musée, *Centennaire Fantin-Latour*, 1936 (523); Leicester Galleries, 1936 (68); Paris, Palais National des Arts, *Chefs d'œuvre de l'Art français*, 1937 (625); Paris, Musée de l'Orangerie, *Donation Paul Jamot*, 1941 (105).

LITERATURE: L. Benoist, in *L'Amour de l'Art*, 1926, p. 173; C. Roger-Marx, *Daumier*, Paris, 1938, p. 26.

Lent by the Musée des Beaux-Arts, Rheims

For a small painted version of the figure of Don Quixote in this drawing, see No. 96.

229 Don Quixote and Sancho Panza

Sancho regardant partir Don Quichotte

PLATE 35B

Pen and ink over charcoal: 19·3 by 25·6 (7⅝ by 10⅛).

PROVENANCE: Roger Marx.

EXHIBITION: Galerie Dru, 1927 (81); Orangerie, 1934 (120).

LITERATURE: Fuchs, 342a; Lassaigne, pl. 159; C. Roger-Marx, *Daumier*, Paris, 1938, p. 24; Maison, *Drawings*, ill. 143.

Lent by Monsieur Claude Roger-Marx, Paris

A study for the painting in the Payson Collection, New York. See No. 98 and note.

230 Don Quixote in the Mountains

Don Quichotte dans les montagnes

Charcoal and stump: 25 by 44 (9⅞ by 17⅜). Verso the same drawing in charcoal, reversed and squared for transfer.

PROVENANCE: Joyant.

EXHIBITION: Bibliothèque Nationale, 1958 (218).

LITERATURE: Maison, in *Burl. Mag.*, January 1954, p. 14 and Figs. 9 and 10.

Lent by Monsieur Maurice Loncle, Paris

Study for the paintings in the Metropolitan Museum of Art, New York and in the Rijksmuseum Kröller-Müller, Otterlo (see No. 99).

231 Don Quixote and Sancho Panza

Pen and wash: 26·4 by 37·2 (10⅜ by 14⅝).

PROVENANCE: Gallimard; Cassirer.

EXHIBITIONS: Orangerie, 1934 (124 bis); Zürich, Kunsthaus, *Von David zu Millet*, 1937 (58); New York, Knoedler Galleries, *Loan Exhibition of the Collection of Erich Maria Remarque*, 1943 (16).

LITERATURE: Maison, *Drawings*, ill. 145.

Lent by Mr Erich Maria Remarque, Ascona

Daumier made two black chalk tracings of this drawing; one, of Don Quixote and the donkey only (Paris, M. Loncle), the other of the whole drawing (Buenos Aires, Dr Bruck).

Index to Lenders

The Plates

Plate 1   'We want Barabbas!' (2), *Museum Folkwang, Essen*

Plate 2 The Miller, his Son and the Ass (7), *Corporation of Glasgow, Burrell Collection*

Plate 3 Two Nymphs pursued by Satyrs (6), *Montreal Museum of Fine Arts*

Plate 4 Young Girls bathing (10), *Monsieur P. Lévy*

Plate 5   The Painter before his Easel (50), *Phillips Collection, Washington*

a

b

c

d

Plate 6 (a) The Watering-place (11), *Miss M. S. Davies*
(b) Bather at the Watering-place (12), *Lord Wharton*
(c) Horsemen in a Wood (14), *Private Collection*

Plate 7 (a) Billiard-players (33), *Private Collection*
  (b) The Chess-players (34), *Musée du Petit Palais*
  (c) The Beer Drinkers (30), *Dr F. Nathan*
  (d) Lunch in the Country (31), *National Museum of Wales*

a

b

c

Plate 8 (a) The Rescue (16), *Christabel, Lady Aberconway*
             (b) The Kiss (18), *Musée des Beaux-Arts, Berne*
             (c) The Secret (29), *Monsieur L. C. Stein*

a

b

c

d

Plate 9 (a) Group of Women and Children (19), *Rijksmuseum H. W. Mesdag*
             (b) Children under a Tree (22), *Toledo Museum of Art, Ohio*
             (c) Children coming out of School (20), *Monsieur A. Daber*
             (d) Woman carrying a Child (28), *Private Collection*

a

b

c

Plate 10   (a) Portrait of a Woman (25), *Glasgow Art Gallery*
                 (b) Woman wearing a blue Ribbon (27), *Dumbarton Oaks Collection*
                 (c) Study of a Man's Head (39), *National Museum of Wales*

a

b

c

Plate 11 (a) Portrait of a Painter (49), *National Gallery of Scotland*
    (b) The Bell-ringer (43), *Private Collection*
    (c) A Writer (38), *Wildenstein & Company*

a

b

c

Plate 12 (a) Doctor Diafoirus (60), *Dr and Mrs H. Bakwin*
(b) Le Malade Imaginaire (62), *Philadelphia Museum of Art*
(c) The Serenade (46), *Mrs A. Kessler*

a

b

c

Plate 13   (a) Two Print Collectors (55), *Prof. Dr H. R. Hahnloser*
(b) The Print Collector (56), *Fairmount Park, Philadelphia*
(c) The Connoisseurs (53), *Museum Boymans-van Beuningen*

a

b

c

d

Plate 14 (a) Head of a Clown (67), *Lady Berlin*
(b) Head of a Buffoon (66), *Mr E. Reves*
(c) The Troubadour (64), *Cleveland Museum of Art*
(d) The Wrestlers (65), *Ordrupgaard Collection, Copenhagen*

a

b

Plate 15   (a) Scene from a Molière Play (63), *Musée du Louvre*
          (b) Leaving the Theatre (61), *Mr and Mrs C. W. Engelhard*

a

b

Plate 16   (a) A Third-class Carriage (70), *Mr A. Beard*
          (b) A Third-class Railway Carriage (69), *National Gallery of Canada*

Plate 17 The heavy Burden (74), *Monsieur E. Gutzwiller*

a

b

c

Plate 18 (a) A Lawyer reading a Document (86), *Dr R. Bühler*
(b) Three Lawyers in Conversation (83), *Phillips Collection, Washington*
(c) Members of the Bar (84), *Mr and Mrs C. Goldman*